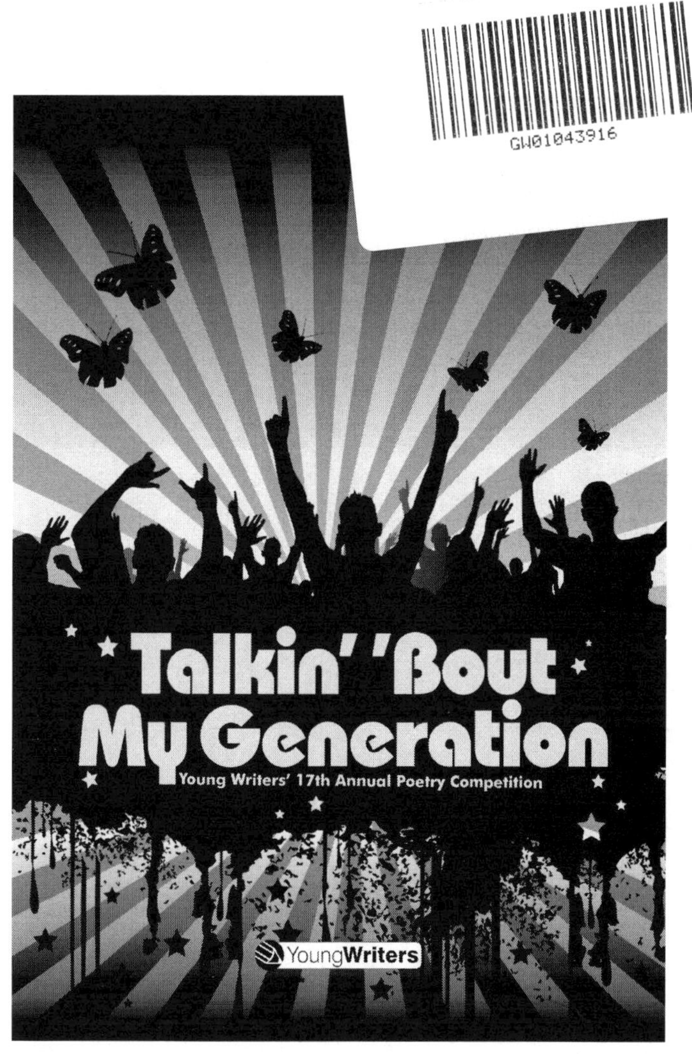

Poems From Eastern England

Edited by Annabel Cook

First published in Great Britain in 2008 by:
Young Writers
Remus House
Coltsfoot Drive
Peterborough
PE2 9JX
Telephone: 01733 890066
Website: www.youngwriters.co.uk

SB ISBN 978-1 84431 703 5

Foreword

This year, the Young Writers' *Talkin' 'Bout My Generation* competition proudly presents a showcase of the best poetic talent selected from thousands of up-and-coming writers nationwide.

Young Writers was established in 1991 to promote the reading and writing of poetry within schools and to the young of today. Our books nurture and inspire confidence in the ability of young writers and provide a snapshot of poems written in schools and at home by budding poets of the future.

The thought, effort, imagination and hard work put into each poem impressed us all and the task of selecting poems was a difficult but nevertheless enjoyable experience.

We hope you are as pleased as we are with the final selection and that you and your family continue to be entertained with *Talkin' 'Bout My Generation Poems From Eastern England* for many years to come.

Contents

The Poems

My Dog

My dog is called Jess
She likes to make a mess.
Dotty, dotty, dotty, that's my dog
She likes to play with a log.
My dog is so big
She loves to dig, dig, dig.
My dog lies in her bed
Until she gets fed.
My dog barks, barks, barks
She likes it in the dark.
My dog comes to her name
She loves to play a game.
My dog is so rough
Because she is tough.

Tash Manning (12)

One True Friend

I have this mate,
She's really, really great,
She always makes me laugh,
She is like a million bubbles in the bath,
She is wonderful,
She has always helped me,
Never leaves me,
She would never deceive me,
She always treats me,
She is always there in my time of need,
Especially when she gave me this little bead,
It wasn't just anything,
It was simple really,
But it was true,
She's one in a million!

Lianna Excell (11)
Alameda Middle School, Ampthill

Art

Get out your brush,
Create something lush,
For your family today,
And the enjoyment of the display.

The work here is done,
The end of the fun,
But you've made a big mess,
And that's what's best.

Wish wash,
Bish, bash, bosh,
All your hands are clean,
Look down and see if your face is seen.

Put your stuff away,
Make sure you don't delay,
Say goodbye to everyone,
Now's the time for some more fun!

Liam O'Dell (10)
Alameda Middle School, Ampthill

Computers

Nintendo Wiis and PlayStation 3s,
Fancy computers and technical bloopers,
Mario, Sonic and Mr Bionic,
Some people love,
And some people hate,
Is it Colin McRae or Rally Game 8?
Amusement arcades or GBAs,
MMORPGs or cleaning virtual dog's fleas?
All these computers will make you forget,
Please do your homework - if you don't, you'll regret,
Just listen to a simple warning,
If you play on your Xbox, you'll regret it next morning!

Matthew Bailey (11)
Alameda Middle School, Ampthill

Reptile Rap

Some are tall,
Some are tubby,
Some can be a bit chubby,
Snakes see with heat,
Lizards have feet,
But they all like to eat,
Lizards are like little wizards,
Are they here?
Are they there?
For all you know, they could be anywhere!
One day when I was getting the barber to cut my hair,
He offered me a pear,
Then I jumped like ten foot in the air,
All because a lizard was on my chair,
So then he ran back to his little lair,
Carrying a nasty stare,
So beware,
Snakes slither,
They could give you a shiver,
But most of all they go and strike,
With a flash!

Ben Walker (10)
Alameda Middle School, Ampthill

Sweets

S weets come in lots of colours,
W hen you eat them, they fizz, pop and crackle,
E very time you eat one, your tongue turns a different colour,
E ating sweets can make you sick if you eat too many,
T ime to stop eating sweets,
S top! Stop! Stop!

George Amiss (11)
Alameda Middle School, Ampthill

Night

Night steals the sun,
As the rays disappear, the moon comes out,
The birds' song is dead,
The owl's hoot alive,
The light is dark,
The night is here.

Night has no face,
A shadow looms over him,
No shoes he wears,
A gown is his,
Pale white skin,
Short tufty hair,
Eyes that glow like the moonlight,
Night is here.

Some fear night,
And have nightmares,
Some love night,
And sleep into a dream.

As night flows through distant dreams,
The darkness of night unhinges its seams,
As dark turns to light,
A tall white figure goes into the night.

Anna Bailie (11)
Alameda Middle School, Ampthill

Small Bones

I heard it squeaking in its nest,
I tried to sleep but I could not rest,
It was my hamster in its cage,
Young and alert, only one year of age.

Six months later, it had grown fat and tall,
I saw it running in its ball,
I felt its soft fur in my hand,
I imagined it digging in the sand.

Another six months and it became a chore,
Cleaning it out started to bore,
It ate its food all day long,
But still squeaking and squeaking its high-pitch song.

One week and it was feeding time,
Our hamster lay still and the clock began to chime,
It was six o'clock and I knew my hamster was dead,
A tear dropped on its cold head.

We buried it on a cold morn,
It reminded me of when it was born,
I was guilty and I felt really bad,
I thought of the friendship we should have had.

But in my heart it is still alive,
In my heart, it is still alive.

Nicholas Pollard (11)
Alameda Middle School, Ampthill

The Day I Met A Skega Lega Sauri

I went to the zoo,
So many animals there,
A hare was there,
He bounced on a chair,
Which gave me a scare.

A lion, a tiger, sleeping all day and night,
I saw a cow, it went miaow,
And I thought, *wow that's weird,*
I told my mum, she said, 'Don't worry son,'
The next enclosure,
Looked kind of empty,
Apart from there was a move,
No mane,
No fur,
No scales,
No tails,
One eye,
And six legs,
I asked the keeper,
'What's that?'
He said, 'It's a Skega Lega Sauri,'
That strange animal looked blue with yellow stripes,
It made a noise, a squeak, not a roar,
Or maybe an eek,
That was my day at the zoo.

Owen Woodruff (12)
Alameda Middle School, Ampthill

The Tour De France

There is a race called The Tour de France,
The all time legend is a man called Lance,
He won it seven times, from 98 to 2005,
Yet he's lucky he's alive,
Many look up to men like him,
Who are fighting cancer for months on end,
But thanks to the money he has raised,
By many people he is praised,
Yet all has changed in the last few years,
With drugs and scandals and riders' tears,
In 2006, Floyd Landis broke the rules,
And by the end of all the blood tests,
He was stripped completely of it all,
In 2007, crowds gave a cheer,
But by the end, the world quivered with fear,
Sponsors are pulling out,
And we know what it's about,
In last year's tour, there was not one or two but three scandals,
That were taking all the news channels worldwide broadcasts
and pulled out from filming,
The future was uncertain,
But hope came right at the end of the season,
There is now a brighter future to the sport,
And the world's toughest sporting event is reborn, once more.

Ryan Owens (12)
Alameda Middle School, Ampthill

Winnie The Pooh

He is a lemon meringue pie,
A sweet honey face that makes people cry,
A tiny yellow bear with puffy cheeks,
From behind all the tree trunks, he peeks,
His shirt is a crimson red,
He eats all the honey when he needs to be fed,
He lives in a tree in the Hundred Acre Wood,
Living off all the honey and pud,
He is the only bear,
To have the inside of a tree trunk as his own lair,
His very best friend is named Piglet,
Who is so very tiny, he looks like a Twiglet,
As well as that, there is Tigger,
He is orange and a whole lot bigger,
They go back a long time ago,
All you do is look down low,
You know that there's a mighty chance,
That you'll be able to take a glance.

Amy O'Dell (10)
Alameda Middle School, Ampthill

Winter

Blistering winds, a cold light,
Struggling through the blizzard's night,
Hitting, smashing all in its path,
Waiting, waiting till the last gasp,
Biting, fighting all in the way,
People watch in dismay,
Frosty freezing winter's bite,
Wandering through the cold light.

Harrison Welham (12)
Alameda Middle School, Ampthill

Mystery Ghost

I'm quiet and mysterious,
I walk the streets alone,
Some say I don't exist,
Others say I groan,
I hide in houses,
I hide in trees,
I know the names of all of the seas!
I'm quite hard to see and find,
But people have said they've seen me,
I prowl the graveyards every night,
There's blood upon my knee,
People fear me, but I do no harm,
I'm a friendly ghost, so please keep calm.

Kira Bolsom (11)
Alameda Middle School, Ampthill

Horse

Clip-clop, clip-clop,
Down the street,
Clip-clop, clip-clop,
Go his feet.

His flowing mane,
And silky tail,
I do not know,
Why he's for sale.

What's his name?
I do not know,
I need to see him,
In the show.

Daisy Hodgson-Smith (11)
Alameda Middle School, Ampthill

In The Middle

I hate my life,
It's the worst of all,
I'm not really popular,
I'm not even cool,
I'm just in the middle.

I'm not fat, yet not skinny,
But no one really cares,
They probably wouldn't even notice me,
If I strangled a bear,
I think I'm just in the middle.

I'm not top maths and I'm not in the bottom,
I don't support a football team,
But I kind of like Tottenham,
I think I'm just in the middle.

I'm not really tall
And I'm not really short,
But I still managed to play on the tennis court,
I think I'm just in the middle,

I don't have any pets,
But I like to walk dogs,
And I used to have a ginger mog,
I think I'm just in the middle,

But to be truthfully honest to you,
I love to be normal,
It feels fresh and new,
I don't hate my life,
I love it!

Lauren Maidment (12)
Alameda Middle School, Ampthill

You're Not There

Your voice still sounds in the hallway,
Your laugh still echoes on the stairs,
Your face is still in my mind,
But still in my house, my life, you're not there.

It's not like you're far away,
In fact, you're rather close,
But when I come and see you,
Your mind just isn't there.

I try not to think about it,
I try not to care,
But everything reminds me of you,
And that you're never there.

I used to hear things that I shouldn't,
Yelling in the night,
But now you're gone, there's silence,
And that doesn't sound quite right.

I know I'm not alone,
And I know life's not fair,
But still I can't stop pining,
Because you're not there.

I want to scream and screech at you,
Because you're still not trying,
You think you've lost your family,
You won't stop crying.

I'm a lot older now and I know things can't be the same,
But my feelings haven't changed,
I want you to hear me, loud and clear,
I want you to be there!

Amber Reidy (12)
Alameda Middle School, Ampthill

Wars

If it's not France V Finland,
It's Iraq verses England,
Wars are difficult and cause dispute,
Wars are the opposite of what girls call cute,
Wars will kill and many die,
War is the opposite of a nice warm pie,
While many people pray and pray,
Soldier's fight and die by day,
Many dads and soldiers risk their lives,
To fight the countries we despise,
War brings sadness,
War brings death,
War usually begins with much, much theft,
The question I ask is why leave alone,
Your wife and children to a horrible tone,
Of a police cars' sirens beating for,
To find your dad has died at war?

Callum Donbavand (11)
Alameda Middle School, Ampthill

My Zoo

My dog is very cute and fluffy,
I've had him since he was a puppy,
My rabbit is a big, fat bunny,
When he eats, he looks really funny,
My hamster has a well sweet name,
She makes me look like I'm insane,
My fish is gold and his name's Mars,
He's so fast, he races cars,
My parrot is so bright, it hurts,
I find her hidden in my skirts,
My cat has big, black, beady eyes,
I'll be very sad when she dies,
Now you've heard about my zoo,
You steal my pets and I'll kill you.

Lucy Davies (12)
Alameda Middle School, Ampthill

Worries

Sometimes in a bottle,
Maybe deep within,
Sometimes floating away,
Could be thought a sin.

Whispers in your ear,
Round and round and round,
Speaks to you sincere,
Saying without a sound.

Always up above,
Maybe down below,
Again, again, again,
But you will never know.

Sometimes in a bottle,
Maybe deep within,
But you will always know,
It will never win.

Jasmine Alfieri (12)
Alameda Middle School, Ampthill

My Fat Fish

My fish, my very big fish,
My fish was a 7lb fish,
My fish was a carp, a common carp,
My fish fought a lot as I reeled it in,
My fish was about 2 foot long,
My fish was slimy but very fat,
I named my fish Harry but he wasn't one,
I was about to put him back,
I thought, *let's give him some water and take some pictures,*
I had taken the pictures,
So I put him back and said goodbye.

Louix Bingham (13)
Alameda Middle School, Ampthill

The Girl

She danced around in her pink satin slippers,
While her brother ran round in their grandfather's nippers,
She did all this and so much more until the day she died,
She walked, ran, sat and played under an old green willow tree,
She used to listen to the sound of the small stripy bumblebees,
She would do this night and day,
She did all this and so much more until the day she died,
She lost all her family, the poor young soul
And because of this, she would stand there and cry and cry,
She cried on the beach, usually it brought back her memories,
While I watched her tears fall in the tide,
They would drift away in the ocean,
She did all this and so much more until the day she died,
She sat in her bed one dark, cold night and
whispered, 'Nobody cares!'
All the other children would not go in there because nobody dared,
She sat there and cried all night and deep in her tears,
She did all this and not much more,
For that was the way she died.

Dee Adams (12)
Alameda Middle School, Ampthill

Bugs

I saw a snail on a whale,
That moved its tail while
The snail wailed. The snail
Had a big shell, while I looked,
A hole appeared in the ground,
And down I fell, down to Hell,
I landed with a thud,
On top of a bug.

Leon Hymus (11)
Alameda Middle School, Ampthill

Modern Day Life Poem

Sit down, buckle up, shut up, you don't want to catch
flies in your mouth,
Life is like a roller coaster,
It goes up, it goes down, emotions go round and round,
Then suddenly you come to an abrupt stop -
hey, what was that all about?
Shirt tails in, shirt tails out, don't get caught as the pink
slips are about!
Don't swing on your chair, as you might smack your head,
So nothing's changed there cos that's what they've always said.
Five a day . . . no way! Oh OK, a Brussels sprout on
Christmas Day (*Urrgh*),
Stand in line, don't fidget mind,
No clip across the ear here, only detention - oh what a bore!
Don't be a statistic, don't eat that biscuit,
obesity is lurking everywhere.
'Mum, can I go to the park?'
'Make sure you come home before it's dark!'
'Have you got your mobile? Are you sure?'
'Walk on the footpath, don't talk to strangers, don't accept any lifts!'
'Phone me when you get there, don't be late!'
'Have you got your mobile? Are you sure?'
Homework! Oh not again, what a bore,
Don't they realise that I've got to improve my Nintendo Wii score?
Umbro, Adidas, Reebok, Nike, I love them all,
But my pocket money is far too small,
I have lots of friends that I love to see,
That's when I'm truly me,
Not during the week, homework must be done,
Only the weekends can we have fun,
I'm only twelve,
But manhood is knocking on my door,
Sit down, buckle up, shut up, you don't want to catch
flies in your mouth.
Life is like a roller coaster,
It goes up, it goes down, emotions go round and round.

Connor Griffith (12)
Alameda Middle School, Ampthill

School Life

Oh how I hate school,
Although my friends think I'm cool,
How I have to get up early,
With my hair really curly,
Thinking about the day ahead,
Oh how I want to get back into bed,
Oh how I hate school,
How we all cram into that tiny hall,
I really love sport,
I run and run around the badminton court,
I really like art,
I think it's kinda smart,
I really hate the homework,
If people are mean, I call them a jerk,
People say school is boring,
Even worse when it's pouring,
Overall school is OK,
Only on a good day!

Jodie Dimmock (12)
Alameda Middle School, Ampthill

Cancer

A sting in your arm,
A pain in your chest,
A growth in your blood,
A home for Death's bed,
A death in the family,
A cry in the night,
A stone in your shoe,
A scream of fright,
Cancer.

Toby Morgan (12)
Alameda Middle School, Ampthill

Skiing

Going down the snowy mountain
with your long skis
nothing could be better
not even eating cheese
turning and sliding
bending and gliding
skiing is so great
nothing could be better
not even playing with your mate
feeling the wind in your hair
skiing down the mountain without a care
going to places
walking to the chairlifts with different paces
feeling the skis on your feet
and the people you may meet
skiing is so great!

Joseph Nejier (11)
Alameda Middle School, Ampthill

Bradley Chalkers

Bradley Chalkers the American guy,
Hated wearing any type of tie,
He walked to school till his friend Jeff walked by,
He hated school,
His classmates thought he was not very, very cool
And Jeff thought he looked a fool,
He could say, he would spit on people,
If they didn't pay,
Bradley Chalkers the great big bully,
He was the one that sounded all woolly.

Bethany Line (10)
Alameda Middle School, Ampthill

The Cat On My Lap

There once was a cat,
It came and sat on my lap,
The cat was so good, it didn't need a slap,
The cat wanted a snack,
So I bought it some catnap.

The cat said yum-yum,
As it sat on its bum,
Then it started doing a sum,
And I said, 'Go for it chum.'

Then I started chewing gum,
It tasted like a rubber plum,
The cat was so dumb,
It couldn't do the sum.

The cat wanted to go,
So I made it a bow,
It walked home very slow,
I didn't want it to go though,
And I was left all alone.

Alice Hawkes (11)
Alameda Middle School, Ampthill

This Morning

This morning I got up,
And I saw a duck,
Quacking away,
Then later that day,
I heard something downstairs,
So I walked that way,
And it was the telly,
But after that I heard my dad's belly!

William Maidment (11)
Alameda Middle School, Ampthill

Black Boots Bill

We were sitting round the fire,
When we heard a noise,
At first it was just tap, tap, tap,
But then it turned to this:
Crack, bang, smash, kazoom,
As glass flew through the air,
And when we turned you won't believe the figure we saw there,
Black boots, brown belt (as thick as it could be!)
A mangled beard and squinty eyes,
His hands were wrinkly,
And in one hand he held a gun,
The biggest you did see,
And as the looming figure stepped through the window frame,
I scooped up the little one,
As he began to scream,
And then, as suddenly as he had come,
The man had gone again,
And that my friends was the last I saw,
Of Black Boots Bill!

Tegan Gowing (10)
Alameda Middle School, Ampthill

Dogs

I adore dogs,
Even though they sleep,
They bark when they talk,
And ride in Jeeps,
They love pork,
Have eyes like a hawk,
And look like they
Need a walk.

Niamh Duncan (10)
Alameda Middle School, Ampthill

When I Placed A Bet On A Box

When I placed a bet on a box,
I went to my lawyer, who said,
'I'm sorry you're going to lose this,
You'll have to break up with Ned.'

It's only a box though I placed a bet on,
'It's only a box,' I said,
'I know what it is, you placed a bet on
But you'll still have to break up with Ned.'

'Maybe we could call off the bet,
Using a comfortable bed?
Maybe we can try that,' the lawyer replied,
'Rather than break up with Ned.'

'I'm never going to gamble again,
I've learnt my lesson,' I said,
'I won't place a bet on a box,
I'll gamble with toothpaste instead.'

Arron Aatkar (10)
Alameda Middle School, Ampthill

Spring

Piglets and lambs blossom to life,
And the farmers get a wife,
Flowers make the world go round,
The wind blows but makes no sound,
The green grass grows,
The sweet smell of a rose,
As it falls to my toes,
Pigs snort,
What a lovely thought,
So let's go fly a kite,
Up to the highest height.

Harley Edwards (11)
Alameda Middle School, Ampthill

The Man Down My Street

There's a man down our street,
Who you wouldn't want to meet,
As he doesn't like a treat,
Nothing even small.

You see people go in,
And think about turning round,
They come out with no grin,
Like they went over the bound.

When you walk past his house,
You don't see a thing,
Not even a mouse.

His house is dark,
Dark as the park,
I don't want to go there.

So that's the man down the street,
Oh what a pleasure he would be to meet.

Leah Chavda (13)
Alameda Middle School, Ampthill

I'll Never Be A Poet

I'll never be a poet, I just know it,
Nothing I write ever rhymes,
It feels like I'm doing lots of crimes,
I'll never be a poet, I just know it,
They try to teach poetry, instead I run up a tree
To get out of their way,
But some day, some way,
I will learn poetry instead of running up a tree,
Soon I know I shall love poetry,
I shall write about love, doves and the heavenly skies above,
But one thing I shall always know,
Even though I'll love it, I shall never be a poet.

Rebecca Scroxton (10)
Alameda Middle School, Ampthill

The Poem

My teacher told me to write a poem,
But I don't think I can,
My teacher told me to write a poem,
But I don't have a plan.

Everyone is writing,
Everyone in the room,
Even my teacher's having a go,
I just sit in gloom.

I really don't mind English,
And that is honestly true,
But the problem with poetry is,
I just don't have a clue.

Cat's already finished,
Her poem on a magical land,
But she won't let anyone read it,
I wonder if she'll give me a hand.

Our time's nearly over,
My paper's as white as snow,
Then inspiration hits me,
And off I go!

My poem's nearly finished,
My pen is running out,
But I have to keep writing,
'Time's up,' my teacher shouts.

I haven't finished my poem,
Everyone's handed theirs in,
I have to keep on writing,
Or my efforts will be in the bin.

I finished my poem!

Alice Redman (12)
Alameda Middle School, Ampthill

Monday Morning

Monday morning comes around,
Then I hear the awful sound,
The alarm goes off loud and clear,
Ringing sounds in my ear.

I walk slowly off to school,
Being late is just too cool,
My friends are waiting at the gate,
Hoping that I'm not late.

The bell for assembly it soon rings,
Next you know you're singing hymns,
Off to lessons I must go,
Many facts and figures I need to know.

Soon the bell will sound for break,
A rest from lessons I can take,
I meet my friends and have some fun,
Playing, chatting in the sun.

In maths and RE, the clock ticks by,
How I wish time would fly!
At last lunchtime is now here,
We all rush out with a great cheer.

Science and French, what a drag,
It will soon be time to pack my bag,
The bell at last sounds the end of day,
Now I'm off on my way.

With my mates, I laugh and talk,
Quickly home I may walk,
Ten minutes later I'm chatting again,
With my mates on MSN.

Discussing highlights of the day,
You wouldn't believe the things we say!

Emma Turner (12)
Alameda Middle School, Ampthill

We Are The Teachers

I'm a teacher, listen to me telling off those who disagree,
Naughty people break detention,
You will get in trouble,
Ooohhh!

I am the head of the school,
You are little, I am tall, I will even catch you in the hallway,
For PE you need shorts and shirts,
You must even face the mud and the dirt.

For mathematics you need glue,
You may even need to go to the loo,
English, science, French and RE,
They are the lessons in school.

Patrick Hopwood (11)
Alameda Middle School, Ampthill

The Ghost Of A Memory

Memories,
Just lingering there,
At the back of your mind,
They just seem to stare,
At your future, your present, your life,
The things that are carefree,
They should fly like a kite.

However, they don't
They're there like a ghost,
They just haunt the moment you cherish the most,
When you're alone, don't know what to do,
Those memories return and you think,
I remember you.

Emily Chapman (12)
Alameda Middle School, Ampthill

My Generation

My generation likes gadgets and gizmos,
iPods and tripods, computers and scooters.

My generation like initials and text speak,
PCs, MP3s, and wi-fi is gr8.

My generation likes fitness and sport,
Swimming, football, judo are taught.

My generation likes food and snacks,
KFC, Burger King, McDonald's in a pack.

My generation is too cool!
My generation rules!

My generation likes holidays and travel,
Portugal, Spain and America in planes.

My generation likes the telly,
Hundreds of channels that don't cost a penny.

My generation likes going to school,
Friends and lessons, music sessions.

My generation likes caring and climate,
Recycling and cycling and all things green.

My generation is too cool!
My generation rules!

My generation likes clothes and fashion,
Bootleg, skinny and flare.

My generation likes MSN and Bebo,
Everyone chatting to lots of people.

My generation likes banks and money,
Spending and saving, saving and spending.

My generation is fun,
I wouldn't want to be in another one.

My generation is too cool!
My generation rules!

Isabelle Martin (11)
Alameda Middle School, Ampthill

I'm Snow White

I'm Snow White,
And no one cares,
People just say,
'You're a normal girl, go play over there.'

I'm Snow White,
But no one cares,
My parents just say, when I'm ill,
'You're alright, you're a normal girl,
Just take this pill.'

I'm Snow White,
But no one cares,
I ask people for help,
They just say, 'Go away you dumb chick.'

I'm Snow White,
But no one cares,
All I want
Is someone to be there.

I'm Snow White,
But no one cares,
I want to run away,
And live in a castle, far, far, far away.

I'm Snow White,
But no one cares,
I get bullied and my fairy tale,
Is now at its very end.

Alice Cornwell (12)
Alameda Middle School, Ampthill

A Rap About Myself

Fricker-fricker fresh,
Bom bom chick, a bom bibbom chick,
I got a mega bling-bling and baggy-waggy pants,
And I love to sing,
And I love to dance,
When I look in my locker,
Can't find my books,
All the teachers gave me dirty looks,
When I eat my lunch,
I always eat pie,
Without it, I'm gonna cry!
And I always wanna have a little snack,
When the music's on, it's my favourite track,
I got a PS2 and a Nintendo Wii,
When I'm playing, I know I'm free!
But as you would also agree,
I like to eat my yummy, yummy tea!
Boring lessons are always slow,
Like a teenager would also know,
When I'm in my English class,
The times run away, it's too fast,
Say word,
Say word,
Say word,
Say fricker-fricker-fricker-fricker-fricker-fricker,
Word!

Mason Hornibrook (11)
Alameda Middle School, Ampthill

My Dad

My dad has a full-time job,
My dad is rather odd,
My dad has a family but
He still finds time to fit in 8 hours of TV a day.

My dad has a wife,
My dad has a knife,
My dad likes his grub but,
He still finds time to fit in 8 hours down the pub.

My dad has a son,
My dad has lots of fun,
My dad loves to be rude but,
He still finds time to fit in 8 hours of being in the nude!

Harry Whan (12)
Alameda Middle School, Ampthill

Love

Love is happiness,
Love is care,
Love is everywhere,
Love is special,
Love is fun,
Love is friendship for everyone.

Love is romantic,
Love is a hug,
Love is a smile from cheek to cheek,
Love is Valentine's Day.

But the best love
Is one kiss.

Ben Ford (11)
Alameda Middle School, Ampthill

Mix Up In Time!

They arrived home from school one day,
And sat down to watch TV,
After they went to the freezer,
Took out pizza and chips.

When they had eaten, they played on a PSP,
At night-time they would disappear to something called a 'rave'.

The next day they went to school,
Texting their mates on the way,
But then one said,
'Hang on a sec, what you doing with a phone?
Have you forgotten - we're in ancient Rome!'

Rebecca Carr (12)
Alameda Middle School, Ampthill

My Little Box Of Memories

Under my bed, in my box -
You will find two odd socks,
A dandelion that we called Fred,
A potato gun that was fired at my head,
Sellotape people that Sophie made,
An empty Lynx can that Catherine sprayed,
A picture of Beth with long hair and a duck,
A teddy bear that Nomie wanted to chuck,
A pair of old flip-flops from lazy days of summer,
A picture of Fly Girl that used to hummer,
And a Hunnies work out from Squidia and Claire,
All of these memories take me somewhere.

Kate Badger (13)
Alameda Middle School, Ampthill

The Windy Road Of Life

Beauty is a wonderful sight amazing to behold,
Even though these words are not all that old.

The sharp thorns as violent as the nights,
But beautiful petals provide a warming light,
It twists and it turns with amazing grace,
Everything is wonderful, even its race,
From the smallest of beings it does grow,
Even though the time sometimes goes slow.

Sun, rain and light make it rise tall,
As long as we're here to catch it, it shall never fall,
It takes the good, it takes the bad,
It tries to look happy even when it's sad,
Up and down the windy road,
Carrying its heavy load.

Two sides to show are pretty and sharp,
The sound is as beautiful as a golden harp,
But when time is running out,
It will cry and shout,
And slowly age takes its toll and creates new life,
No need to worry about any more trouble or strife.

Life is like the journey of a rose,
We take the good and the bad,
We get used to new words like awesome, cool and rad,
The journey isn't always straight,
There is usually a bump in the road,
But whatever happens, we must always stand tall.

What is the meaning of life?
Nobody knows,
But whenever I hear that question,
I will always think of the rose . . .

Sebastian Sear (11)
Alameda Middle School, Ampthill

Kids These Days

Talkin' about phones, MSN, computers,
Getting the latest gadgets, accessories,
Boys dreaming about being footballers,
Girls dreaming of becoming pop stars,
Thinking of how to avoid the school bully,
What lesson have we got next?
Will the teacher set homework?
Then again, that new Porsche is nice,
But what about the Aston Martin DB9?
I wonder if Robbie Williams drives one?
His new song is good,
So is Mika's, do do dum do dum,
I wonder if Kylie will have another?
Our band's the best though,
MSS, the new school band,
And I'm the singer, wow!
Our first rehearsal is tomorrow,
Oh no, it clashes with footy,
What am I to do?
I'll ask Mr Smith if I can miss the match,
I bet he'll say no, blast!
Oh well, there's always next time,
Or is there? Mr Smith is strict!
All the teachers are, I am used to it,
But who cares about school when there is home,
Computers, PS3, Xbox 360 Elite,
The best bike, got everything on it,
Just two hours till the end of school,
I just wanna get home . . .
Then again, doesn't everyone?

Matthew McCready (11)
Alameda Middle School, Ampthill

My Weekend

Saturday morning, the weekend has begun,
A busy day of having fun,
Netball training with all my friends,
Hoping the day never ends,
Beep of the horn, it's time to go,
The dog needs walking, we all know,
Running through the forest, the sun in my face,
Chasing faster and faster the dog loves to race,
It starts to rain, we all run fast,
It seems the rain is going to last,
Muddy shoes and dripping hair,
Where's the sun gone? It isn't fair,
Off to a party, running late,
Down to the ice rink to have a skate,
First start, wobbly and scared,
Quite a shock, we weren't prepared,
Getting better, now this is fun,
Faster, faster, is how it's done,
The fun ends without a fall,
Marshmallows and hot chocolate for all,
Tired and weary, we all drive home,
To watch a film and chat on the phone,
A warm bath I shall take,
A lovely dinner, my mum shall make,
The warmth of the fire sends me to sleep,
Another great day with memories to keep.

Ella Phelan (11)
Alameda Middle School, Ampthill

My Friends

Friends are priceless gifts,
Which cannot be bought or sold,
Friends are hopes and dreams,
Which are forever told,
Friends are there, through good and bad,
Sometimes they make you laugh,
Sometimes they even make you sad,
Friends have got each other's back
Any time, any day,
Friends argue and fight,
But they know down inside, that it isn't right,
Friends can change a frown,
Upside down,
Friends don't spill secrets,
And they don't tell lies,
Friends will guard your secrets,
Like their life depends on it,
Friends come and go,
But true friends leave footprints in your heart,
Friends always listen,
And never laugh at you,
Friends are hard to find,
True friends are harder to leave,
But best friends always share the moments,
The laughs, but best of all,
They share the memories in their heart.

Shannon Stickland (12)
Alameda Middle School, Ampthill

My Generation

This generation may be different to yours,
But it is still a generation,
My generation can be clear,
My generation can disappear,
My generation is a roller coaster,
Can be explosive,
Causing rage,
Good things happen,
Bad things happen,
Joyous occasions along with sadness,
Lack of respect is bringing disruption,
In a world that is a rat race,
People are born and people are taken,
People invent things that move us forward,
Hard to keep up with,
New gadgets and electronics are made non-stop,
Made every day of the year,
My generation would be boring,
If there was nothing to do,
Some people buy all the gizmos,
But some people can't afford them,
In my generation, people are in debt,
They can't afford most things,
So they save money for the things they want most,
Music is a big thing in my generation,
We can't do without it 24/7,
There are big TV shows every year,
Big prizes are won and comments are made,
My generation should be loving and caring,
Is this generation one you would like to live in?

Emil Chavda (11)
Alameda Middle School, Ampthill

The Cricket Poem

As I grow up watching
Match by match
Waiting for my chance to shine.
Now I am a star
Hitting ball by ball
Four by four
Six by six
Smash by smash
Century made!

As I spin the ball
Flicking from my wrist
Around the batsmen
Through their legs
Smashing the stumps
Bails go flying
Into the wicky's face
Hitting the stumps
Batsmen are out!

Standing here
Waiting for the ball
To come my way
Hit up high
Coming towards me
Coming down fast
In my hand caught
No fumble!
Doesn't touch the ground
In one hand
Caught - batsmen out!

Niall Sherry (11)
Alameda Middle School, Ampthill

Talking About My Generation

T alking about my generation and the animals we all love,
A nd how we are destroying their habitat,
L ost forever, never to return,
K illing them by changing their world,
I ce is melting, the planet is warming,
N ow we need to help them before they are
G oing, going, *gone!*

A lbatross, the largest flying bird is near to extinction,
B irds in our gardens are not so common,
O rang-utans' homes are disappearing under the chainsaw,
U nless we act it will continue,
T igers live in 40% less habitat than a decade ago.

M arine life is being polluted,
Y our world is changing.

G lobal warming and greenhouse gases are changing our world,
E ndangered animals may be lost forever,
N ature is at risk as seasons change,
E verything is under threat,
R ainforests are disappearing fast,
A rctic animals like polar bears and seals need protecting,
T urtles survived the dinosaurs but could soon be gone,
I llegal ivory trade is threatening the elephant,
O nly we can save them or they will
N ever be seen again!

Jennifer Kent (12)
Alameda Middle School, Ampthill

AC Milan

Milan, Milan,
I have been to the stadium named San Siro,
I am the biggest fan,
You can go there to see your local heroes,
They have touched my heart,
Touched my soul,
Changed my life and all my goals!
We sometimes lose so I have my doubts,
But we always find clues,
And at the end of the game, the crowd all shout,
They are really good at football,
And they are big champs,
Even if they lose, they are still cool,
And Kaka is miles better than Frank Lamps,
They are trustful and kind,
They sometimes play dirty,
But aren't they fine
And Gattuso makes people hurty!
If you support them you are with me,
Kaka is my star,
As you will see,
He is as fast as a 100mph car,
You will see the whole squad,
Gattuso, Kaka, Pirlo and more,
They are all gods,
But some of them get sore.
Soo - Milan Milan Solo Cantare!

Lino Grillo (11)
Alameda Middle School, Ampthill

A Typical School Day

When walking down the hallway,
Kids are messing about,
Lockers haunting you down and down,
They're sitting all around.

Sport is always active,
Jumping, running and throwing,
Stretches you should be knowing.

Playtime is so hectic,
Balls flying through the sky,
It's never too late to go and wait,
In the library as time passes by.

Maths is always boring,
Numbers, algebra and work,
When there is extra time,
I should be getting on with my homework.

Science is an explosion,
With chemicals, safety goggles and friends,
If there is any damage,
We will be sure to mend.

Art is calm and quiet,
With paints, colours and glue,
It is always so frustrating,
When trying to find the right blue.

History is so interesting,
With facts, drama and fun,
Listening to all the facts,
Make it as easy as the sun.

French is always different,
Since it's in a different language.

That is my school day.

Ella Sealey (11)
Alameda Middle School, Ampthill

The Best Bowler In The World

As I bowled and rolled
I got told
I was the best bowler
in the world

As I ran and span
almost killed a man
but he hit the ball
with his frying pan

Lots of people have BMWs
but I prefer lbw's
when I got an lbw
my mum crashed her BMW

I always bowl a
yorker or
a low full toss
but sometimes I bowl a short

I always wear
my sunglasses
when everyone
uses their helmets

I always wear
my arm guard
I got it off
Matthew Hogard

I always make
a v shape
so I don't make
a mistake

Every game we play
we always win
anyone I face I bowl out
because I am a winner.

Samuel Foad (12)
Alameda Middle School, Ampthill

The Old Days

Things were better in my day,
That's what people say,
But they didn't have computers then,
Facebook or eBay.

They had to shop at the corner shop,
Just to buy sweeties and pop,
But we can buy it online,
Everything from bread to a mop.

Instead of going by sea,
You can go on the tunnel very quickly,
It's nice to go to France,
To be confined to this island wouldn't suit me.

Smoking used to be cool,
They never learnt about it at school,
But we're a health conscious nation,
So now it's just all taboo.

Foreign cuisine was very few,
In fact you could say it was really new,
Chinese, Italian, Indian too,
All available to satisfy you.

Corporal punishment was near its end,
It used to drive kids round the bend,
Now physical punishment's a no, no,
It's just gone out of trend.

Talking about me,
Talking about my generation,
So just to conclude my poem,
I wanted to be sure you're knowin',
Things are better in my day,
That's what my generation should say.

Katherine Rowe (12)
Alameda Middle School, Ampthill

My School

Monday, Tuesday, Wednesday, Thursday,
And of course, Friday,
I walk to school on each of these days,
To learn even more and more.

At school I have two best friends,
Called Vanessa and Katherine,
We have lots of fun together,
And we are always there for each other.

We have five lessons each day,
Like English, maths and science,
Some lessons are great and interesting,
Whereas others are tiring and not much fun.

At break time the bell will ring,
And we will all run out to play,
My friends and I like to talk,
About things we have done over the weekend.

At lunchtime it is food time,
When we eat our pack lunch,
Some people have sandwiches,
And others have crisps and chocolate.

The teachers at our school are females,
Although there are some males,
The female teachers are kind and caring,
While the male teachers are strict and nasty.

This is what I do at school,
Each of the weekdays,
I learn new facts each day,
To prepare me for later life,
I really find school fantastic,
And I always look forward to the next day!

Kate Templeman (12)
Alameda Middle School, Ampthill

My Friends

Through good times and through bad,
They help me when I'm sad,
They're always there, me reassuring,
They bear me through, my long school days.

They're always fun to have around,
They'll be with me, in a bound,
Together we have so much fun,
I'm glad that I, school friends have found.

Thomas Green (12)
Alameda Middle School, Ampthill

Night

Night is nasty,
Night is scary,
Night is a burglar that steals all the light,
Night has a dark shadowy face and black squinting eyes,
Night creeps around slowly and secretly,
Night is as silent as a mouse.

Oliver Ali (10)
Alameda Middle School, Ampthill

Night

The moon comes out at night,
When we're all tucked up tight,
The stars come out and show their light,
So let's go fly a kite,
I try to see with all my might,
But it is simply out of sight,
So I gave up and called it a night.

Georgia Ferris (11)
Alameda Middle School, Ampthill

My Mates

My mates are cool,
They play netball,
Shan is sweet,
She's really neat,
Secondly there's Faye,
She brightens up my day,
Next there is Shannon S,
She is totally the best,
Han is great,
She's one of my best mates,
Loz is cool,
But today she's ill from school,
There's also Lily,
Who's very silly,
I have a lot more,
But they all live in a Tesco store,
Only joking!
My mates are really great,
But the best part is they're mine.

Charlotte Beard (11)
Alameda Middle School, Ampthill

My Friends

My friends are cool,
They rule the school,
They make me chuckle,
They have big knuckles,
They are there all the time,
They like to rhyme,
I can't get rid of them,
They live in a den,
I like them lots,
Like Jelly Tots.

Faye Lawrence (12)
Alameda Middle School, Ampthill

My Friends

My mates . . .
Through good times and bad,
Through happy and sad,
You stand,
You walk,
You listen,
You talk,
Happiness,
Smiles,
Pains and tears.
I know you will be there,
Through the years,
When one of you are sad,
I will wipe away your tears,
When one of you are scared,
I will help your fears,
When one of you are worried,
I will give you hope,
When one of you is confused,
I will help you cope,
When one of you is lost,
And can't see the light,
I will be your torch,
Very, very bright,
This poem hasn't been a task!
Why? You might have asked,
Because I'm your friend and I care!

Hannah Wilkinson (11)
Alameda Middle School, Ampthill

True Love

Her face is more beautiful than the shining moon,
Bouncing off the ocean sea,
Her hair is softer than a dove,
Her heart warmer than the sun,
Her eyes brighter than the brightest star,
Her smile worth seeing more than a thousand diamonds.

George Lawson (11)
Alameda Middle School, Ampthill

Nowadays

Look at me, I am ninety years old,
I am also going very, very bald,
Kids these days, with all these rings,
Always with bling and those things,
Look at them with their baggy clothes,
Some of them just play with big fat globes.

Most of them have spiky hair, just looking cool,
Back in those days, I looked like a fool,
Everyone wanting the latest technology,
To get that I had to learn some biology,
Look at all those gangsters stealing stuff,
Next time they do that, they'll go away in cuffs.

Nowadays you can go to school for free,
Back in my day I would be chopping down some trees,
Some people don't care about their education,
Because it might destroy their reputation,
People these days are pretty dangerous,
To me, I think this is really outrageous.

Justin Chan (11)
Dame Alice Owen's School, Potters Bar

Life

Where are we from?
And why are we here?
Why do we love?
And why do we fear?

We laugh and we cry,
But life goes on,
We live and we die,
But life goes on.

It slips quickly by,
Like a babbling brook,
Before your eyes,
Yet you cannot look.

Life, a shimmering elixir,
All men search for it,
Life, a mystical oil,
Through which all is lit.

Stephen Hawes (12)
Dame Alice Owen's School, Potters Bar

Help Me

My eyes so tired and dull,
I shed a tear, crystal clear,
My lips feel like banana skin,
My head throbs,
The sun is shining so brightly, blinding,
My mouth as dry as sand,
No one to look after me,
I am on my own now,
My stomach is a lion's growl,
The water I drink is not like water at all,
Help me, help me please, if you can hear me.

Catriona Wastell (11)
Dame Alice Owen's School, Potters Bar

Bird

Sometimes I'm low, sometimes I'm high,
Sometimes I rest and sometimes I fly,
I live in a nest,
Who am I?

I fly around the world,
Seeing everything,
Sometimes it's great,
But sometimes it's not,
Who am I?

My species get chased and killed by cats,
Can't get grades because I can't get SATs,
Who am I?

I've travelled the Earth, even to Spain,
But I never have felt so much pain,
I am a bird.

Tommy Harrison (12)
Dame Alice Owen's School, Potters Bar

Meaning Of Life

Life is a conversation,
Now here's some inspiration,
What is my duty in life?
Is it just TV, homework or The Wii?
Knowledge is a key,
The true secret is inside,
To understand who you are,
To have faith and believe,
In the pleasures of life,
Make your mind your friend,
Not your enemy.

Life is short,
So make it worthwhile.

Emma Clayden (11)
Dame Alice Owen's School, Potters Bar

Dreams Of My Heart

If I was God,
I'd crown myself queen,
I'd raise the good
And banish the bad,
I'd cast away poachers,
And bring back the extinct,
By using the powers,
Which I'd possess,
I'd brighten the sky,
With a click of my fingers,
And rearrange the twinkling stars,
In the infinite heavens,
I'd create an array of new colours,
To inspire the artists,
And compose a new language,
Speaking of love, never hate,
And now the dream of my heart,
Comes to an end,
As I gaze around my bleak cell,
And contemplate my crimes.

Catherine Medayil (11)
Dame Alice Owen's School, Potters Bar

The Bear

The great bear, lumbering through the pines,
Though thought to be ferocious, evil it is not,
Only if you threaten it, then it will attack,
The mother with its cubs, watching,
In case they wander from her sight,
The father, fishing in the river,
A salmon in his mouth to be carried back to his cubs,
All this in a gun's sight, a man's gun,
Bang, bang, bang, bang,
All fall, dead.

William Alfred Smith Hughes (11)
Dame Alice Owen's School, Potters Bar

A Better Place

Wouldn't Earth be a better place,
If we weren't one money-guzzling race,
So if we spent all that extra cash,
To help the poor, why waste it on trash?

Stop all that poverty and the hunger,
There are people suffering, our age and younger,
So don't be greedy, give to the needy,
Help people get back on their feet, super speedy.

So your little money, may buy you some honey,
But why not put it to a better use,
Go on, go to your local charity shop, make *no* excuse!
If you are thinking there is a good deed to be done,
Then you are correct, don't be dumb!
Go down there, donate some dough,
Some celebrities do it, but that's just for show.
Your small amount could change the world,
If you use it wisely enough, it will all unfold.

Domenico Sterlini (12)
Dame Alice Owen's School, Potters Bar

Snow

On a perfect morning from my bedroom,
I looked out to the shining and glistening snow,
Everything the snow touched was now a crystal,
Shining white and I longed to go outside,
I touched the snow; I could feel every flake cold and crisp,
From the snow I made a snowman, it looked so much like me,
It was like a dream turned into reality, everything was perfect,
The snow was like a blessing from the mountains and the sky,
I have never seen so much snow in my life and it feels unreal,
A few days later all the snow had melted,
My happiness just vanished,
Now I really long for the snow to come back next year.

Alex Carter (11)
Dame Alice Owen's School, Potters Bar

Football

Football is amazing fun,
Especially when played in the sun,
You kick the ball towards the goal,
It hits the net just like a rocket,
We scream and shout, oh what a racket,
The crowd goes wild, you hear the cheers,
The fans are ecstatic,
They have waited all these years,
Three more seconds left, the crowd holds their breath,
The final whistle blows,
The game is over, your team has won,
Oh wasn't that fantastic fun,
Football is the game where winning is the aim,
Anyone can play whatever their age,
So give it a go and join today,
You will be surprised how much you like to play.

Nathan Medford (11)
Dame Alice Owen's School, Potters Bar

The Universe

In the beginning life was plain,
Then things came along and it wasn't the same.

Fish, sharks and mammals too,
Added to the world for there to be things to do.

Then there was food, trees and land,
Added on top was lots of sand.

Then we had humans, who made more and more,
Who also made houses with an open front door.

The universe was created, and will never be deflated.

More and more things will come, and will be done.

Beatrice Lugli (12)
Dame Alice Owen's School, Potters Bar

Think About It . . .

Think of a busy road,
With car after car,
Honking at each other to move.

Think of an aeroplane,
Cruising through the air,
Carrying holidaymakers to distant lands.

Think of a factory,
Tall and grey,
Generating clothes in the latest fashion.

Think of all the smoke and CO_2,
Clouding up the atmosphere,
Trapping in the sun's rays.

Now think of all the innocent little penguins,
Stranded in their slowly melting world,
With no chance of survival or escape,
Their only hope is if *you*,
With all the other 60 billion people on the planet,
Change your ways.

Thomas James (12)
Dame Alice Owen's School, Potters Bar

Left Alone

All on my own and nowhere to go,
Everyone's gone, friend and foe,
Nothing to eat and nowhere to sleep,
All on my own, I shall just weep,
Whatever it takes to become strong,
I shall do, right or wrong,
As I'm alone, on this very day,
I will lovingly say and pray,
I didn't do wrong, I didn't do right,
But I don't deserve this, not tonight.

Roberto Di Muro (11)
Dame Alice Owen's School, Potters Bar

The Babies

Don't leave me here,
But don't put me there either.

I would like some food,
Not some tissues.

This seat belt is too tight,
I think I'm going to puke.

Just give me some milk,
I don't like dummies.

Don't suffocate me with this toy
That smell is me.

I'm 6 months old, remember it,
Don't pinch my cheeks.

You're going to drop me,
Waaaaa.

Finally you change my nappy,
This is more comfortable.

I'm tired,
I hate these pyjamas.

Give me my milk again,
And teddy.

And blanket,
And zzzzzzzzzzz.

Sean O'Dea (12)
Dame Alice Owen's School, Potters Bar

Better World

I would stop war and crime,
I would make people feel fine,
I would stop poverty and disease,
And have a world that would please,
I would make hospitals better,
And make England less wetter,
I would stop tidal waves and hurricanes,
And get rid of busy roads with country lanes,
I would share out riches to all the poor,
And put the homeless in houses,
Making them homeless no more,
I would grow lots of trees for the world to breathe,
And global warming problems would relieve.

Bethany Meighan (12)
Dame Alice Owen's School, Potters Bar

Abandoned

The men who let me play,
They have all gone away,
The people never cared,
Leave me abandoned, lost and scared,
I remember days, playing in the sun,
But now it's over and I'm on the run,
See that scraggy mutt on the corner,
With not one,
Single mourner,
That's me.

Michael Crout (11)
Dame Alice Owen's School, Potters Bar

The Cat

A stray cat limps through the streets,
Hiding from anyone he meets,
Scared and wet and thinking about,
Why his owner chucked him out.

The cat's thoughts are dark and sad,
As he remembers the times he'd had,
Kicks and screams race through his head,
He thinks about food instead.

Shivering with cold, he leapt the fence,
The hunger inside him was immense,
Oh how he wished he had a friend,
Someone there for him to the end.

He'd find someone, with a nice face,
He'd have a mat by the fireplace,
Then suddenly, with a friendly grasp,
A human picks him up at last!

Elizabeth Rowlands (11)
Dame Alice Owen's School, Potters Bar

In The Future

In the future, I'll be older,
For as time goes by perhaps I'll get bolder,
For at the moment, I'm quite shy.

Once I'm older, I'll be wiser,
Once I'm wiser, I'll be lazier.

As the days go by, I'll get frailer,
Sooner or later, I'll disappear,
And that's the end of me.

Harry Page (12)
Dame Alice Owen's School, Potters Bar

My Generation

My mother tells me 'When I was your age
I lived in a world where cassettes were the rage!'
But in this modern world, iPods never leave pockets,
Holed up in your room, television burns eye sockets.

Small innocent toddlers, spiritual souls white as snow,
But growing up in this dangerous world,
Grime begins to show,
From toddlers to teenagers, the mother is always there,
But when they must leave the nest, they leave her
guidance and care.

Fried food, abuse, thieving, death of others,
They're exposed to this, without protection of a mother,
They'll find a husband or wife,
A house after much strife,
Because this is the world they live in.

Emily Faint (11)
Dame Alice Owen's School, Potters Bar

The Future

I think of the future,
What does it hold?
Will I die young?
Will I grow old?
Will I be happy, successful and rich
Or will I be foolish and live in a ditch?
With all of these questions there's just one way to know,
What will happen to me when older I grow?
The only way to know the answer for sure,
To finally open that ever closed door,
There's nothing that anyone would need to give,
Except in this life to happily live!

Jordan Barker (12)
Dame Alice Owen's School, Potters Bar

A World For The Future

If I could change the world,
I would change many things!
I would spread my wings,
And stop all bad things!
Like terrorism, poverty and war!
We want no more,
Come on now you power monger,
Donate money to world hunger!
Don't throw your rubbish on the floor,
You know that it's against the law!
Stop the war in Iraq,
Get those soldiers on a long journey back!
Global warming can be rather mean,
So turn off your lights and all go green!
Evil gangs aren't cool,
Politeness is the real rule!
So wrap up those guns and knives,
Some victims have children and wives!

Leslie Smith (11)
Dame Alice Owen's School, Potters Bar

My First Day At Secondary School

On my first day at secondary school,
We met the Head in the Edward Guinness Hall,
From the oldest in one school to the youngest in the next,
We were all uncertain, worrying, panicking.

We were bombarded with information,
Timetables and rules,
For lunch I had pizza but there were other fuels,
We ran through the woods, whilst finding our way,
Before the big kids came back the next day!

Emily Bannin (12)
Dame Alice Owen's School, Potters Bar

This Is How I See The World

My generation
This is how I see the world,
The sea is a sky of waters,
The sun is a ball of gold,
The trees are always perfect,
Whether they are new or old!

The mountains are gravely pyramids,
The moon is a sphere of dust,
For all of these wonderful miracles,
In nature I can trust.

The rivers are like blood in a steady stream,
The stars are a collage of glitters,
In spring there is just so much colour,
Flowers in bloom and insects that flitter.

The night is a curtain of sapphires,
The night is a cloak of shadows,
The night is a magical darkness,
A darkness that always glows.

The snowflakes are crystals of perfection,
The flowers are colours and scents,
From an ant carrying, to a tornado's howling,
These are nature's beautiful events.

The plants are marvellous due to pixie magic,
In toadstools and trees fairies dwell,
Every pollen, petal and all,
Gives off the most marvellous smell.

The rain has tiny footsteps,
Giving off the tiniest sound,
The weight and height of a melody,
Is something that my curiosity has not yet found,
This is how I see the world.

Misa Roberts (12)
Dame Alice Owen's School, Potters Bar

My Little Friend

As his scales brushed against my cheek
And his colourful little legs climbed my face
The jaw of this creature opened,
He let out a terrifying screech.

The noise ached my ears,
As did the colours with my eyes,
They stared intently into mine,
My senses tingled as he jumped,
Across and away, forever.

Once I finally realised you'd gone,
I looked staring at the canopy above,
The roof of trees,
Protecting me,
From the sun,
The rain,
The weather,
Leaving out the light,
Until rustled by the wind,
Blowing the sun inside
The cave of darkness,
A macaw flew by,
Flying with colours,
Gracefully,
Reminding me of my little friend whom I will never see again.

Bavnisha Tulsiani (11)
Dame Alice Owen's School, Potters Bar

Misunderstood

When I help a lady cross the road,
She hits me with her umbrella,
Thinking I'm going to hurt her,
Thinking I'm up to no good,
I'm just misunderstood.

When I put up my hand in class,
To give my thoughts and opinions,
The teacher looks at me,
Thinking, I'm up to no good,
I'm just misunderstood.

When I tell my parents, 'I'm going out!'
They start to get suspicious,
Asking me, 'Where are you going?' and, 'Who will you be with?'
Thinking, I'm up to no good,
I'm just misunderstood.

When I get on the bus, the driver thinks I'm rude,
Because I forgot to show my pass,
He keeps looking at me in his mirror,
Thinking, I'm up to no good,
I'm just misunderstood.

Just because I'm in my teens,
And I like to have a little fun,
Doesn't mean I'm always,
Up to no good,
I've been misunderstood.

Anies Sohi (13)
Dame Alice Owen's School, Potters Bar

The World, How And Why It Works, Through The Eyes Of A Teenager

Bluntly speaking turning 13 means nothing more than turning eight,
Except symbolically it means more, you become slightly more late.
Teenagers:
The word strikes fear into some minds
And some people carry on chewing on their bacon rinds.

Are they all menaces?
Are any of them menaces?
Well no and yes,
Some of them are, but they're the minority
So the priority
Of those flashy rich governments should be
To do something about them,
Not us, the smart reasonable teenagers.
Sadly the difference is very difficult to tell,
Until so many years have gone by.

But then once they start setting off fireworks,
They have gone way too far,
They worry all of us, not just you adults,
They are dangerous, to us, you and themselves,
So do something,
Now,
Before it is too late . . .

Phillip Crout (12)
Dame Alice Owen's School, Potters Bar

The Meaning Of Life

Why are we here?
Is there someone up above laughing at our every word?
Is it all just some big game?
If it is, then why the pain?

Why are we here?
Was this meant to be?
Or was it just a scientific catastrophe?
All this made by one mistake, how can you believe it?

Is there an explanation?
How can it be proven?

Today's kids, troublemakers or are we just misunderstood?
Do we deserve titles we receive?
Lazy, disrespectful, surely we can't all be bad?
Do we do it to impress or are we just in distress?

Are we just like little kids crying out to be helped?
Maybe we just need a helping hand?
But who will give it to us as we are looked upon so badly?
Is there a way to get out of this perception?

Crying out for help,
A helping hand to lead us through the darkness.

Ben Purkiss (11)
Dame Alice Owen's School, Potters Bar

Yesterday

Yesterday I met a man, the strangest one I'd seen,
He stood a few feet taller than I, not large - but not quite lean.
He had no name, he had no age, I never learnt his tale,
If I were asked for information I would surely fail.

One frosty night in mid-December (I think a storm was brewing),
The mellow fellow had a plan - a plan he planned on doing.
Through my window he slunk and snuck and shimmied like a fox,
And conjured up a fearful simple weapon from his box.

A blindfold - I could swear it was! I saw it through my fingers,
Which shielded my eyes from the man whilst in my room he lingered.
The unfamiliar man approached my shivering shaking face,
Speedily he covered it, as if it were a race.

He twiddled his fingers behind my head, inside me pumped my fear,
He tied the blindfold way too tight and squeezed out a small tear.
He did this with great confidence, this man - he had no doubts,
He did a knot (what was the name?) I learnt it once in Scouts.

Before I knew it he was gone, he didn't say goodbye,
And to this day I've thought and thought, but cannot work out why.
I reached behind my smallish head to untie these tight knots,
'Was there one, or were there two?' I realised there were lots.

From that day on the blindfold stayed, the reason I don't know,
But now I understand the mellow fellow was a pro.
The way he knew just what to do since he walked through my door,
Gave me every single clue that he'd done this before.

And now there is no image to accompany my noise,
I cannot do what most youths do; have fun, or play with toys.
I am a plane which cannot fly, a dog which cannot bark,
I'm a child who was left alone - abandoned in the dark.

Micha Frazer-Carroll (13)
Dame Alice Owen's School, Potters Bar

Reason To Fear . . .

What's that noise? Are they coming back?
I step carefully towards the door,
Pain in my stomach from starvation and hunger,
Pain in my sides from being hit and kicked,
Pain in my heart from being unloved . . .

I can hear shouting, I start to whimper,
I back away from the door, knowing that it's going to bang open,
And I will be kicked aside like a dirtied rag,
Terror floods through me as the door opens,
And as cold is released into the hall,
A dark shadow looms over me.

I whine and cower into a corner,
Hiding from what I know is coming,
A hand reaches toward my face; I shut my amber eyes,
A sudden energy rages through me and I dart between
the shadow's legs,
And through the open door I run.

Fresh air fills my lungs,
I can hear the shadow yelling, but I know it won't come after me,
The pain in my legs starts to grow, but the feeling of freedom
dances inside me
A feeling that I've never felt before.

New smells fill me with anticipation,
But then I start to pant, tired and drenched with a sudden weakness,
A new fear starts to grow inside me. What do I do now?

I can see two small shadows advancing towards me,
I start to shiver, too scared to move backwards,
A hand reaches towards my face; I shut my amber eyes,
But I don't feel pain.

The shadow wraps its arms around me;
My heart fills with warmth,
I nuzzle the shadows' neck and lick its warm cheek,
I feel loved and cared for; I know that now I am safe . . .

Amy Mace (12)
Dame Alice Owen's School, Potters Bar

Khayelitsha

I walk 6 miles there and back,
Two people by my side,
The hot sun blazes down on us,
Like fire in its pride.

People see us as a shadow,
Nowhere near as good as them,
When hunger strikes us like a bolt,
They just ignore my kind of men.

We live in a face of the Earth,
Which is upsetting, violent and poor,
Our houses we make out of rubbish,
And the ground as our floor.

Our families grow and grow,
With crying faces to feed,
We're always hungry, afraid and alone,
But we don't get the help we need.

We're always thirsty, our mouths are dry,
Every hour, every day, forever,
We get ill by drinking dirty water,
From the brown tea river.

We don't know why we don't get help,
For the food and water we have to have,
But we always pray and hope for it,
So someday we may be gifted.

Beatrice Savory (12)
Dame Alice Owen's School, Potters Bar

My Generation And Yours

We can work together,
Live peacefully forever,
And work as a determined team,
Learn from one another,
But be independent brothers,
Share all of our ideas and dreams.

You make out that in 'Your day',
All of the youth were well-behaved,
But a lot of today's are too, didn't you notice?
You say we don't respect you,
But we do; you should show some for us too,
As we could get along, if there was more justice.

You wash your hands of our childish ways,
Ever think - it's because of how we were raised?
We can have intelligent discussions without being violent,
We are constantly too loud,
And stand out from the crowd,
But you would still think badly of us if we were silent.

But parents seem to understand,
They always have some help to hand,
And can see through to our innocence - know we are no crime,
So next time you happen to hear,
A young mind with an impossible idea,
Try not to criticise, you never know what will
happen in a 100 years time.

Chloe St George (11)
Dame Alice Owen's School, Potters Bar

Chocolate!

Chocolate! Chocolate!
You are a treat that I adore.

Chocolate! Chocolate!
I seem to want more, more and more.

Chocolate! Chocolate!
You lighten up my day.

Chocolate! Chocolate!
I eat you at the bay.

Chocolate! Chocolate!
You make my mouth water!

Chocolate! Chocolate!
I never eat a quarter.

Chocolate! Chocolate!
Are you Cadbury's or Crunchies?

Chocolate! Chocolate!
You always give me the munchies.

Nikhil Sharma (12)
Dame Alice Owen's School, Potters Bar

About My Generation

Thugs, hoods and chavs,
Stealing old ladies' bags,
Innocent kids are put to shame,
It should only be the bad ones that get the blame,
Good kids help the elderly,
And their parents too,
Bad kids kill people,
Because they think they have nothing better to do,
Kids can be good,
They are not all bad.

Christos Loizou (12)
Dame Alice Owen's School, Potters Bar

Youths, Past, Present And Future

Today's youth are the talk of the people,
It's like babies are the future and we're just a sequel,
The part of the story that wasn't meant to be included,
Stuck on the streets all alone and secluded,
A typical youth would hang around with a gang,
Walk around in a hood and arrive with a bang.
But not all are like that and most have a purpose,
Not all want to work in McDonald's or end up in a circus,
Youths believe a label is the worst thing you can have,
Being called a goth, emo, townie or chav,
Kids are still people and don't mean to scare,
All we young people want is to be treated a bit more fair,
So next time there is some troubled youth in your neighbourhood,
Just remember, we're the future and there is no other,
There is nowhere to run or take cover,
So why can't today's people, tomorrow's and yesterday's join,
And not have happiness balanced on a coin,
Let's just appreciate my generation,
As we are the past, present and future.

Gavin Lock (12)
Dame Alice Owen's School, Potters Bar

The Problem With England

The problem with England is
The gangs that roam the streets,
Hunting for someone to sell
Their expensive products to,
It will ruin their lives,
And drive them insane,
The competition is dead,
So they're free to sell their drugs,
Until there's no one left.

Elliot Hussein (13)
Dame Alice Owen's School, Potters Bar

I Love You

I love you
A phrase used by many,
But, I do?
Said by much less.

A loose declaration,
Or a symbol of bonding.
A romantic elevation,
Or a casual remark.

But what is love?
A feeling,
Said to move,
Or something else.

A lacklustre saying,
With no second thought,
Is it betraying
Its noble roots?

'Back in the day'
It was an eternal vow,
To others you'd say nay
A devotion unsurpassed.

But in this generation,
In this day and age,
It's just an exclamation,
A casual remark.

Nick Wilson (13)
Dame Alice Owen's School, Potters Bar

A White World

White's a sign of purity,
Innocence and love,
White's the colour of many things,
Of daisies and of doves.

White's the white of snow,
Icicles and frost,
White's the colour of your face,
When terrified or lost.

The colour of the clouds -
The maker of your dreams,
A colour of a silk
And the thread that holds the seams.

The colour of a wedding dress,
Billowing and bright,
The colour of the stars,
And the moon that lights the night.

The shimmering of opals,
Lilies and bright light,
The tips of foamy waves,
That disappear from sight.

White's the colour of angels,
From the heavenly sky,
The colour that our dentists want,
On the teeth of you and I.

Katrina Thompson (12)
Dame Alice Owen's School, Potters Bar

Some People

Some bullies pick on you,
With the occasional punch,
They call you names,
And eat your lunch.

Some gangs are dangerous,
And are not afraid to fight,
They do this in alleyways,
Or in dark places at night.

Some people are thieves,
And will break into your house,
They steal all your stuff,
As quiet as a mouse.

Some people are worse,
They cause people to die,
They swear and curse,
They make us want to cry.

All these people,
Are all the same,
Whether bullying or killing,
They should all be ashamed.

Todd Garber (12)
Dame Alice Owen's School, Potters Bar

My Generation!

When my mum and dad were young,
I thought the days,
Were black and white,
Now these days are gone.

It was slower back in time,
Different now,
Earphones jammed in ears,
Phones glued to palms.

iPods dinked in,
Hard to hear what's going on,
Cars out for a spin,
Can just hear the phone ring.

Growing every day,
Trying to keep up,
There is a lot to play,
And a lot coming up.

Can't stop now,
My phones are ringing,
Need to change the song,
Stuff going on.

Annabel Rice (12)
Dame Alice Owen's School, Potters Bar

Racism!

Racism is cruel, racism is hurtful,
Why do we speak it and why should we feel it?
Racism causes wars, it makes gangs and discrimination,
Why would you express it and damage each other?
Who would base their opinion on colour and creed?
When really, people should see through their skin,
And not take any notice of your religion or breed,
What is racism exactly?
Is it a feeling or an act? Is it always hurtful?
Could it be good? And how can we stop it?
Racism is a large form of prejudice,
It is prejudice, discrimination, all in one,
Do you want a world where blacks and whites,
Aren't allowed to associate,
And where both races fight, wanting to kill,
Only for one to rule the other?
Why is there racism in the world?
Racism has to stop!

Danny Gibbons (13)
Dame Alice Owen's School, Potters Bar

Fast Food

Burgers, chips are greasy food,
Fast and easy, for any mood,
Pizza, fish and all things fried,
Young people will eat until they've died.

McDonald's, Burger King, Pizza Hut,
A number of harmful food bars need to be cut,
If we are going to have better youth,
Stop shoving bad food down your mouth.

Benjamin Weddell (12)
Dame Alice Owen's School, Potters Bar

The Unseen Man

I saw a man yesterday,
He had black hair,
Nice looking clothes and
A long walking stick.

He was slapping the ground
With the pole,
While his dog led him around,
Doing lots of things for him.

I suddenly realised something,
That he was blinded,
Struck down in life,
Yet he still didn't care.

I couldn't think how it could be,
Not looking at the sea
And feel the calm warmth
Which it contains.

I couldn't think how it could be,
Not seeing the sun
Shine out so bright,
High above the clouds.

I couldn't think how it could be,
To see utter darkness
Consume your eyes
And everything else.

How could anyone know
What it feels like,
To see absolutely nothing?

Samuel Gan (12)
Dame Alice Owen's School, Potters Bar

Action/Reaction

The meaning of life or fate,
Things clever people have thought over for years.
Why are we here?
Why put us here?
And do we have a set destiny?
A pre-organised path we will inevitably take
Or is everything undecided?
Is the thing that put us,
On this vibrant rock in the middle of nothingness,
An all-powerful being of another world?
Or is all we have grown to know,
A repercussion of pure science?
Was this universe supposed to happen
Or was it purely an accident?
I do not believe in fate or destiny,
Or think that something,
So perfect as the universe,
Could be a simple accident.
But I do wonder how with so many impurities,
Can this planet be the project,
Of an omnipotent, all knowing Lord of everything?
I believe that every action has a reaction,
That if any one person did something differently,
Then people's lives would be altered,
And things would change.
You have to make important decisions in life,
Whether professional or social.
But remember that sometimes,
You can only look back and think,
What if that had gone differently . . . ?

Ben Voce (12)
Dame Alice Owen's School, Potters Bar

The Wandering Magic Of The World

The world is hidden with magic and sincerity,
The life form of such beings which generate and guard
This land beyond the fortresses of our holy home.

The sun's light burns above with the gifts of peace,
Which overwhelms us with such knowledge about outer
Life around us, the mysteries to be dug up and preserved.

Only the silent breeze of the northern light enquires such beauty
Upon our prosperity of life and judgement,
Over many gateways to success and dreams.

Forests of trees in happiness of the joy of children learning
And playing football, chess and many games which
Young-minded beings bring to life.

The love between people can last forever,
The slightest of actions can cause love,
Love comes in different sizes but love can only form on such a world.

But all soon will be lost and forgotten, the treachery of our ways
Has brought down the awareness of such disasters
In countries and homes.

The blazing winds stroke and bind the hope of life and love,
Raging with anger that the world will soon come to a stalk
And only evil will control these walls.

The evilness of climate change will overpower everything like
The grace of nature, the twittering birds which awaken in morn,
The cubs of the Albanian jungle.

But the world can work together to save the life form,
By lowering greenhouse gases in many ways,
The world which we call Earth.

Miten Armoogum (13)
Dame Alice Owen's School, Potters Bar

My Society

In my generation,
We are misunderstood,
We are mistaken,
In our society.

We are thought to be dysfunctional,
And also be thugs,
Appear to be lazy,
As well as taking drugs.

We are not all like this,
It is only some,
Who wish to take this route,
However, some aren't breaking thumbs.

What I have been trying to tell you,
Is don't be fooled,
Because we are not all like this
And never will be.

Philip Sam (12)
Dame Alice Owen's School, Potters Bar

Sound And Vision

You assume that I can't see,
And that's the difference between you and me,
My eyes are open just like yours,
So why do you believe that I'm a lost cause?

The setting sun, that rocky shore,
You take for granted and look no more,
But how do you know what sight may be,
When you don't question what you can see?

So I don't appreciate what will never be mine,
But can you really hear what can be defined?
When thunder and lightning cross the sky,
I doubt that you will feel the awesome cry.

Electricity pulses through my veins,
My fingers tingle, are yours the same?
I hear these sounds that you can't see,
So change your thinking; don't feel sympathy for me.

Edward Steele (13)
Dame Alice Owen's School, Potters Bar

My Generation

'They're lazy, violent, stupid, mean,
That's the young generation'.
This is what most people seem to think,
But this is a generalisation.

Yes, we're not perfect,
But neither are you,
Most of us do care,
And only a few

Don't understand,
That the future is ours,
And our actions now,
Could leave deep scars.

All the rest of us want,
Is for future lives,
To live in a world,
That's free of lies.

A world where no one,
Isn't treated the same,
A world where 'the poor',
Is no longer a name.

A world where extinct,
Is no longer a word,
A world where pollution,
Has gone like a bird.

A world like this,
Is far away,
But my generation,
Want to make it next day.

Laura Clee (12)
Dame Alice Owen's School, Potters Bar

What I Don't Get With The World

What I don't get is . . .

Why rich people who have billions,
Won't help the starving millions,
Why people would go to a shopping area,
Rather than save people dying from malaria.

Why people would rather steal,
Than ask another person how they feel,
Why people who pass a group of 'thugs',
Immediately assume that they are on drugs.

Why people would rather eat at Burger King,
Than go and eat some healthier thing,
Why I am forced to eat my fruit,
When the pain for me is quite acute.

Why some people would start a war,
Without learning from the one before,
Why decisions are made by the Parliament,
Without any of the people's consent.

Why I have to go to school,
Just to be made out to be a fool,
Why I do science homework,
If all I want is to become a clerk.

Why do we get an animal killed,
Just to keep our stomachs filled,
Why do we cut down even more trees,
Just to make some more debris.

The way the world is is a shame,
But I would always keep it the same,
Because if it wasn't it would be really boring,
And that is why I'm so adoring.

Richard Cheatle (13)
Dame Alice Owen's School, Potters Bar

Why Are We Here?

Are we here to change the world?
To manipulate or improve it?
Are we here for laughs, for joy
Or are we here to work?
I wonder how animals perceive the world,
Do they joke, laugh, or play?
Is their life much different to ours,
Or is it just the same?
Do animals in the deepest oceans have deepest intimacy?
Have they thought what I am thinking now,
Or do they only think for food?
Why can't animals create fire, poetry, or read?
Why is it I? Why is it us?
I am honoured to have my body, my brain and my friends.

Michael Ginestier (12)
Dame Alice Owen's School, Potters Bar

What Is Blue?

What is blue?
What is green?
These are the things that I have never seen,
What is a smile?
What is a frown?
What is so funny about this clown?
What is a mouse?
What is a fish?
What does this food look like placed on my dish?
Why do they giggle?
Why do they smirk?
What have they smothered all over my skirt?
Please be nice,
Please be kind,
Please respect that I am blind.

Jessica Prior (12)
Dame Alice Owen's School, Potters Bar

The Children Ditching Childhood

Steaming pressure is erupting from
Volcanic adults, hungry for perfection,
Seeping through fresh teenage skin,
A recent study has proven.

A technological overload has taken
Over their graffiti-covered minds,
iPods, headphones planted into ears
A recent study has proven.

Their small white socks painted with
Maturity and anxiety,
The swirling black cotton,
A recent study has proven.

Mascara thick on thin lashes,
Varnish on pale fingertips,
Eyeliner dribbled along the edges,
A recent study has proven.

Emails defeating envelopes,
Fast food demolishing fruits,
Drugs and alcohol are introduced,
A recent study has proven.

Conclusion?

Overcome the pressure,
Conquer the electric apparatus,
Burn away the dark material,

What happened to good old-fashioned
Paper and ink?
It disappeared with the
Innocence of childhood, I think

What was so vile about playing with toys?
Or so horrific about the image of small choirboys?

Why are the children ditching childhood?
Maybe there's something we misunderstood . . .

Emily Buckley (13)
Dame Alice Owen's School, Potters Bar

Sounds

The rustle of the leaves,
The song of a bird,
They will be,
No longer heard.

The growl of a tiger,
The roar of a lion,
I can't hear these sounds,
So I just start sighing.

The purr of a cat,
The squeak of a mouse,
I can't hear a thing,
That happens in my house.

All around me,
Are music and sounds,
They're everywhere,
And in the towns.

All I hear is nothing,
Nothing, nothing and more nothing,
Emptiness and emptiness,
It's just sad, that's the thing.

Paulina Ogar (13)
Dame Alice Owen's School, Potters Bar

The Streets Of London

These are the streets,
The streets which I walked all my life.
I've been away recently,
And these are my streets once more.

The lake which jewelled my scarred childhood.
When I was here, it would lift my worries away,
I, absorbed in the mystical garden.
No more it lifts my worries, but deepens them.

A gale is passing,
With epic proportion,
Leaves soaring,
This is not my street.

The cars roar by,
Like they are the centre of the universe,
But in an endless rush
This isn't life but true in sanity.

The world's endless rush,
To move,
Isn't the world being changed?
But they won't mind which way.

Eduin Boater Latimer (12)
Dame Alice Owen's School, Potters Bar

Keep Talking

Everyone's talking about us,
Keep talking,
Cliques and mistakes is all we are,
Keep talking,
13, pregnant, anorexic and self-harming,
Keep talking,
'The world has changed since I was a girl',
Keep talking,
Soundtrack of our lives, can you hear it?
Keep talking,
'Give peace a chance', 'meat is murder'.
Keep talking,
Graffiti on a broken home,
Keep talking,
Runaways, taking drugs, 12 and on the game,
Keep talking,
'Are you prepared to die for your beliefs, or just to dye your hair?'
Keep talking,
Be individual, proud of who you are,
Keep talking,
In a world of liars, fakers and plagiarism,
Keep talking,
Blinded by hoodies and bad press,
Keep talking,
So obsessed with how we're ruining the world,
Keep talking,
But we all know they're forgetting,
Keep talking,
We won't have a world left at this rate,
Just keep talking.

Tilly Hunter (14)
Dame Alice Owen's School, Potters Bar

Dog

Abandoned,
Don't know where to go.

Confused,
I really don't know.

Frozen,
The air is growing cold.

Young,
I am not very old.

Dark,
The world is turning black.

Staring,
Down the long empty track.

Alone,
There's no one else around.

Silence,
I don't hear a sound.

Lost,
I don't know where I am.

Move,
Don't know if I can.

Unloved,
They no longer want me.

Depression,
Like the sting of a bee.

Heart,
That my owners tore.

Doomed,
Death is at my door.

Emma Combes (12)
Dame Alice Owen's School, Potters Bar

My Generation

Phones stuck to hands, fingers busily texting:
C u l8r@n-field,
Cars zooming past, swarmed all over roads,
Wheels spinning, headlights flashing,
Heads nodding to the sound of their iPods, earphones glued to ears,
McDonald's and Burger King signs plastered all over the streets,
Doors opening and closing every few seconds,
Forests and trees falling down with every minute;
Global warming attacks stronger than ever,
Smoke clouding the air, sickening lungs,
From people puffing cigarettes.
Crowded pubs every night, people walking around drunk,
Losing jobs and money.
Homeless people on the street, or lounging around popular
Train stations; tramps begging for money,
Without shelter, money, food or job.
Litter all over the streets, ancient chewing gum almost
Engraved into the pavements.
New technology appearing every day;
Improved iPods, i-phones, Apple Mac laptops:
Carbon-cutting power stations.
Fashion changing weekly, shops bombarded with
people at the weekends,
Piercing on noses, ears and tummies.
Tattoos covering bodies, worn by strong burly men,
Or by ladies as a feminine charm.
Welcome to 2008.

Amaarah Hossain (11)
Dame Alice Owen's School, Potters Bar

We Are The Gadget Generation

We are the gadget generation,
We all have a mobile and a PlayStation.

Tapes were how our parents listened to songs,
But now we can download them on our iPods and our phones,
We all have an obsession with MSN,
We no longer write letters with a piece of paper and a pen.

We are the gadget generation,
We all have a mobile and a PlayStation.

To get info a computer is all we need,
We don't get books from the library,
To take a photo, they needed a roll of film and a developer,
Now our cameras are digital and picture-taking is so much better.

We are the gadget generation,
We all have a mobile and a PlayStation.

Children used to play games in the street,
Today we play indoors with an Xbox and Wii,
Films were watched on a cinema screen,
Now we put the disk into our DVD machine.

We are the gadget generation,
We all have a mobile and a PlayStation.

What other gadgets will there be in the days to come,
Will they be entertaining? Will they be fun?

Ambika Mod (12)
Dame Alice Owen's School, Potters Bar

Stuff That Stars Are Made Of . . .

We still are stuff that stars are made of,
Our thoughts and dreams are much the same,
A scattered handful in ten thousand,
Rebels against the common aim,
Our aim is this - to reach adulthood,
In all its glorious, dizzying heights,
To touch the pinnacle of perfection
And claim the glittering bauble light,
Of bygone days that blessed the ancients:
Knowledge, wisdom, kindness, grace,
The right to be heard and independence,
At last free to run life's race.

And yet as children we are happy,
There are things grown-ups can't do,
And while we imitate our idols,
We're satisfied and live life to the full.

Ruth Downie (12)
Dame Alice Owen's School, Potters Bar

My Generation

It's a strange place,
The world right now,
Kids sit watching TV all day,
When I was young, I'd go and play.

It's a strange place,
The world right now,
Chavs roam the streets thinking they're hard,
They couldn't scare a bucket of lard!

It's a strange place,
The world right now,
There's loads of global warming,
The thought is quite daunting.

Dominic Pace (12)
Dame Alice Owen's School, Potters Bar

My Generation

We still need to be loved in the same way,
We still need food, drink and water to live,
But not everything stays the same all the time,
The world has changed because of our inventions,
And that symbolises my generation.

Walking around with earphones stuck in their ears,
Listening to music, fiddling on their iPods,
The latest mobile phones on palms and ears,
Texting, phoning, playing games,
Even checking the latest sports news.

Kids go home and switch on the television,
'The Simpson's', 'EastEnders' or 'Doctor Who',
And after that some chips, burgers yum,
Unhealthy food and no exercise,
Causing more people with obesity.

Children driven to school, also back home,
On holidays abroad by huge planes,
Causing more and more pollution,
Ice caps are melting, sea level is rising,
Deforestation, destroying animal homes.

But this is only what is going on,
In the rich countries around the world,
On the other hand, the other side of the world,
The poor countries are facing many problems,
While we enjoy our life with the latest gadgets.

Lots of people die every day, not of old age,
But of no clean water, starvation and illness,
Wherever we live, we should all be treated the same,
With enough water, food, shelter and healthcare,
So let's all get together and do something about it!

Saki Hayakawa (12)
Dame Alice Owen's School, Potters Bar

Today's Generation

Today has really changed
For better or for worse,
People misbehave,
More than before.

Listening to iPods,
Sticking to phones,
Watching the telly,
With stops and moans.

Bullying and stabbings,
Goths and chavs,
Gangs and emos,
And all the hard lads.

Different fashion,
Strange-looking hair,
Nose piercings,
And murdered teddy bears.

KFC and pizza,
And McDonald's too,
Don't forget lots of veg,
No thank you!

Chloe Williams (11)
Dame Alice Owen's School, Potters Bar

My Generation

Nose piercings,
Belly piercings,
Rough behaviour on the street,
Burgers and pizzas; junk food to eat.

Eyes glued to game console, mobiles glued to hand,
Rock guitars and drums; an ideal band,
Door slamming, yelling, getting drunk at pubs,
Off out the door, off to nightclubs.

Staring at the telly; drugs, no cash and fags,
Parents used to give advice - now it seems like nags,
Arguing with parents, off to sulk alone,
Thinking in their heads 'bout how their parents drone,
Graffiti sprayed on shop window,
All the world is foe.

Going round in gangs,
Setting off big bangs,
Their idea of fun,
Is letting off a gun,
In years past this would be sensation,
Now it's part of my generation.

Maria Dutton (11)
Dame Alice Owen's School, Potters Bar

The End Of The World

It's going to be the end of the world,
But we just don't know when it's going to be,
Hopefully it's when I'm old,
So then I don't have to worry!

I hope it is not soon,
There is so much for me to do,
But then hopefully I get reincarnated,
Because I am a Hindu!

Now I can't even sleep,
Because we don't know when it's going to be,
Imagine my last thing was,
Being stung by a bee!

I wish I could know,
And tell everyone,
Oh what a surprise it would be,
Would they be happy or angry?

It's going to be the end of the world,
I wonder if it's going to be painful?
Oh please I'm begging to God,
I hope it's not acid rainfall!

Jayan Patel (12)
Dame Alice Owen's School, Potters Bar

Today's Generation

iPods stuck in ears,
Mobiles bolted to hands,
Chewing gum everywhere,
Thousands of boy bands.

Endless TV channels,
Far too much junk food,
Teenagers in hoodies,
Calling each other dude.

Everywhere I look,
There's people smoking fags,
And all this stupid alcohol,
It's driving me mad!

People glued to computer screens,
Twenty-four seven,
And children are craving drugs,
At the age of eleven.

Oh why has it become so bad?
Oh why can they not see?
That their life is rushing past them,
And it will soon be history . . .

Ben Osgood (12)
Dame Alice Owen's School, Potters Bar

My Generation

Video games on the TV and mobiles in clutching hands,
Talking 'bout my generation,
iPods and their earphones blasting out some loud music,
Talking 'bout my generation,
Nintendo DS and those things called Wiis,
Talking 'bout my generation,
Yes this is me and all my gadgets, me and all of my generation,
Yes this generation is the best but we can be horrible,
Gold chains and gold rings are known as bling-bling,
Talking 'bout my generation,
Then there are those who ruin it by wielding knives,
Talking 'bout my generation,
Yes that's my generation,
Then there are the types,
Talking 'bout my generation,
There's those chavs, emos, goths and them townies,
Talking 'bout my generation,
They know who they are,
Yer!

Luka Spiby-Vaun (12)
Dame Alice Owen's School, Potters Bar

Time Difference

When I was young, we had no cars,
Our most precious thing was probably jars,
I do not really understand this Game Boy,
I would much rather play with this wooden toy.

There are many new things like Nintendo Wii,
As well as PS1, PS2 and PS3,
They all confuse me with bizarre instructions,
And what are these crazy functions?

There is nothing on Earth that can change us,
Because I just found out about Uranus,
No one knows the distance to say,
Apparently it's a million miles away.

I would much rather stay on the Earth,
Or much better yet AstroTurf,
I am starting to like the future,
But I care more for nature.

Edward Tsang (12)
Dame Alice Owen's School, Potters Bar

Stabbed

I bang on my drums,
Jamming with my band,
While a hooded teen walks,
A knife in his hand.

I grab my Converse,
And run out the door,
But the hoodie has seen,
My friend on the floor.

I run towards my friend,
As fast as a dart,
Only to find,
The knife aimed at his heart.

The knife draws back,
Reaching a deadly height,
And by the time it plunges down,
His life has gone,
Switched off like a light.

When I reach the scene,
The killer has fled,
And have tears in my eyes,
As I bury the dead.

Daniel Levy (12)
Dame Alice Owen's School, Potters Bar

The New Generation

All this new technology,
Confusing and new,
Computers and phones,
What do they do?

All these rude kids,
Each with an ASBO,
Making so much noise,
Baggy trousers low.

All everyone eats now,
Is fast food muck,
Chips and burgers,
Pizza and duck.

All the things they wear,
I see in these brand new shops,
Bleached hair and pierced ears,
Ripped jeans and stripy tops.

What is the world turning to?
Teens do things I wouldn't dare,
Smoking, drinking, having fights,
All they seem to do now is swear.

Nancy Gillen (11)
Dame Alice Owen's School, Potters Bar

My Generation

This is my generation,
We are spread across the nation,
Talking all the slang,
We speak like this 'yo wassup man,
Who did diz?'
We've got the PS3,
Which they didn't have in 1973,
There's all the wars between counties,
We should set this aside,
And then we would be satisfied,
We drink all the booze, take all the drugs,
We walk around like a nation of thugs,
We don't want to take all the drugs and drink all the booze
Because we wouldn't be on the 24 hour news,
It wouldn't make us cool, it wouldn't make us hard,
You would just end up a fat tub of lard,
We go to school all the time,
I hate it but the paninis are divine.

James Goodey (11)
Dame Alice Owen's School, Potters Bar

Emos (My Generation)

I am young and still in my teens,
With my tie and my shirt and my skinny black jeans,
And I listen to music, the one that is rock,
So if you annoy me, I'll give you a shock,
I'll get my guitar and I'll play some loud shrieks,
So all of you go, including you geeks,
I have all my music on my MP3,
And I like to play cool games on my Nintendo Wii,
I like my hair over my eyes,
But my mother hates it, I'm not surprised!

Ben Vize (12)
Dame Alice Owen's School, Potters Bar

Today's Generation (Gangs)

The gangs are on the streets in the dead of night,
Knives in their pockets looking for a fight,
Hiding in the shadows, hoodies round their face,
Waiting for the victim, someone they can chase.

Out of the darkness comes a policeman on the beat,
Looking in the places where the gangs all meet,
The streets are damp and empty, there's nobody left,
The gangs are on the prowl trying to do a theft.

They hide all round the alleys, and under the tree,
Frightening old ladies and everyone they see,
A police car quietly patrols the street,
As a crowd of hoodlums run with their feet.

But what can we do to stop this crime?
To listen to the gangs and give them our time,
To improve their lives and respect their neighbours,
To give them a reason to improve their behaviour.

Nikolas Vourou (12)
Dame Alice Owen's School, Potters Bar

My Generation

What has happened since I was small?
Mobs of people standing so tall,
Young kids, earphones in their ears,
Smoking and drinking cans of beer,
Young ladies, their tummies hanging out,
Men in black handing odd substances out,
Sometimes I wonder how things can change,
Young people killing within their range,
What has happened since my generation?

George Petrie (12)
Dame Alice Owen's School, Potters Bar

Changing Times

Things are so different now,
When I were a lad there were no consoles or DVD players,
Then it was just good old board games,
People play these now and they are still pretty popular,
But it saddens me to see kids spending hours on their computers.

It seems as if as the world gets older,
The youth of this world gets more impatient and violent,
It made me very sad and angry to see a young child,
Throwing eggs at my window on Hallowe'en.

There used to be people laughing and playing on the street
But now their laughter has been silenced,
I go down to the local park to cheer me up
But even the young kids having fun and playing there
Do not help me cheer up.

Will no one hear my cries of how this modern world has turned out,
No one treats me with respect and I am old and
Since last year, lonely, and there is now nothing in my life
worth living for,
The fresh bread of the past has now turned mouldy.

Is there no space in this modern world for an old man?

Ashley Wagner (12)
Dame Alice Owen's School, Potters Bar

My Generation

My generation is different from others,
No punks are to be seen,
They are all replaced by chavs,
Who think they're cool and get keen.

Chavs always wear ridiculous clothes,
Not including skinny jeans,
But they wear their baggy trousers,
Down to their knees.

They think they're cool with their bling-bling,
But they're really not,
I think they should go away,
Before they lose the plot.

In my generation we play on our phones,
Giving our phones a name,
We can also download new music,
And all the latest games.

This is new technology,
Which is getting cleverer more and more,
This is why my generation is,
Better than before.

Peter Jordan (11)
Dame Alice Owen's School, Potters Bar

My Generation

Generation, generation,
What is happening now?
New computers, new games,
What will be found?

Generation, generation,
What will we have next?
Something fun, something new,
Will we get a text?

Generation, generation,
What can we do?
Will it be bad?
Could it be you?

Generation, generation,
Who is to blame?
Was it your mum or mine?
Can we put a face to a name?

Generation, generation,
How will it find us?
Is it coming?
Will it come by bus?

Generation, generation,
Will it warm us?
Can it help or be trouble?
Whatever it is - don't make a fuss.

Is it your future or ours?
Can it be stopped or not?
Will it be horrid?
Or will it be fine?

Laura Adamson (11)
Dame Alice Owen's School, Potters Bar

The Next Generation - My Granddaughter

I was sitting in my house one day,
Watching the setting sun,
When I realised that time was passing fast,
And a new generation had begun.

The kids go out in Converses,
Skinny jeans and bling,
And they listen to songs on the radio,
In which the pop stars can't even sing.

And the language they use! Can't they even spell?
I can't understand a thing,
They use it online and on MSN,
And now there's this new thing called bling.

Last Christmas I gave her a present,
A long green skirt and scarf,
But she said it was out of fashion,
And that it nearly made her barf.

One day she came home and said to me,
'Look what I did today?'
She pulled up her sleeve above her wrist,
Which she'd slit! What could I say?

She said she'd become an emo,
She'd wear black for eternity,
At first I thought it was just a joke,
So I asked her to make me some tea.

'But Grandma,' she said, 'tea's disgusting,
Have some Coke instead,
I know it has loads of caffeine in,
But you're not even going to bed.'

Marianne Barnard (11)
Dame Alice Owen's School, Potters Bar

What The MySpace Profile Doesn't Say

Details:
Headline: Why do you choose to pick on me?
Orientation: Lesbian (according to them).
Here for: An escape from this world.
Gender: Female.
Age: 15 years old.
Location: My bedroom sanctuary.
Education: Secondary School.
Mood: Suicidal.

Interests:

General:
I don't go out much, because I'm scared,
Of the words they shout, it's too much to bear,
Instead I stay at home, write my poetry,
About whatever I want, to fly and be free.

Music:
Gangsters sing about drugs, fights and money,
Kids follow their example, but I don't think it's funny!
Britney Spears 'Toxic' driven into little girls' heads,
Their innocence is lost, tucked away under beds.

Television:
They say that junk food commercials will be taken off air,
But the poor girls are so thin, they really don't care.

Books:
Stories that take me to different worlds,
Away from the suffering, the wars that unfurl,
Tales of people that can never die,
That, when I come back to reality, make me cry.

Heroes:
I am all on my own, there is only me,
Left alone, as miserable as can be,
Left to carry the torment and violence,
That only stops when my tears have silenced.

Whatever happened to the children of today?
There are no longer any smiles, innocently at play.

Alice Rafter (13)
Dame Alice Owen's School, Potters Bar

Their Generation!

(A poem written by an old lady about the children of today!)

The new things of today, they just keep running away,
These great new ideas just create more fears,
Kids graffiti their body with loads of tattoos,
They hang around in their hoodies taking drugs and booze,
With 9/11 and all these terrorist attacks,
Decency and love the world much lacks,
With emos, goths, chavs and geeks,
Us oldies find it hard to turn our cheeks,
Global warming spinning out of control,
Soon we'll be sucked into a big black hole!
The human race will deteriorate!
Nobody can stop it because it is just fate,
In my day kids were seen and not heard,
They did what they were told, now their behaviour is absurd!
With all their PlayStations, gismos and gadgets,
Drug dealers turning our kids into addicts,
Eating nothing, but fast food,
No wonder the whole world is in a bad mood!

Sophie Dowdell (12)
Dame Alice Owen's School, Potters Bar

Monopoly Is Dead

Monopoly is dead,
Hard rock stuck in my head,
Controllers and screens,
Game boards are has-beens.

Monopoly is dead,
People saying 'innit bled',
Texts making thumbs sore,
Faxes are no more.

Monopoly is dead,
So many people three times wed,
People like zombies as they walk,
Earphones stop all talk.

Monopoly is dead,
All I care about is street cred,
The Internet like a huge sea,
Loads of islands set you free.

Monopoly is dead,
McDonald's is what I'm fed,
My earphones in all day,
Hypnotised by my phone's display.

Monopoly is dead,
Credit always in the red,
Global warming on the news station,
Welcome to my generation!

Robert Tomlinson (11)
Dame Alice Owen's School, Potters Bar

My Generation!

Nintendo Wii and PS3,
It's just not how it used to be.

Talking about my generation!

Kids used to play outside all day,
But now inside is where teens stay.

It's all about the latest PC game,
Nothing at all is quite the same.

Talking about my generation!

Having to have the latest craze,
I'm sure this time it ain't no phase.

Talking about my generation!

ASBOs dished out here and there,
Teens are shouting, 'This ain't fair -
We were only playing truth or dare!'

In each generation there's a change,
So stop complaining we're so strange!

Now I just rest my case,
So give us kids some wanted space!

Talking about my generation!

Being something else I shall not pretend,
As I'll be proud of who I am and what I am till the end!

Alishia Hawkins
Earlham High School, Norwich

My Generation

Fashion shirts and mini skirts,
Big black belts and a ring that hurts.
Fancy jeans and swirly swirls,
Brilliant clothes for boys and girls.

Fashion shirts and mini skirts,
Big black belts and a ring that hurts.
Fanciable bargains of shoes, well off,
Big or tall, large or small, it's time to hit
the shopping mall.

Fashion shirts and mini skirts,
Big black belts and a ring that hurts.
High-heel boots and make-up galore,
It's about time you knew the score.

Fashion shirts and mini skirts,
Big black belts and a ring that hurts.
It's a new craze, a fun sensation,
2008 is my generation.

Genevieve Alterman (13)
Earlham High School, Norwich

My Generation

Teenagers get blamed for lots of things
Like vandalising signs,
For stealing, rudeness and disrespect,
But we're not all like that in these times.

Some of us have hobbies,
Want to do well in school,
Actually care about our future
And not just want to be 'cool'.

We get blamed for growing up too fast,
Having babies far too young,
But some of us are sensible
And know our rights from wrongs.

Not all of us will end up bums
Living off the dole,
We want careers with prospects,
In society we'll play a role.

So all you adults who think bad
Of youngster just like me,
Realise we're not all thugs and yobs,
We can act positively.

Lauren Jeary (12)
Earlham High School, Norwich

My Generation

Our generation
Is made out of lots of rotations,
Fashion, money, looks, shoes,
The way you walk and talk.

My friends
Enjoy hangin' out with me,
But in our generation
You have to be funny.

We mess around,
We have fun,
We like to go swimming
And then we run.

But what we love most of all,
We're a big gang,
A big brick wall!

Jordana Reeve
Earlham High School, Norwich

My Dance Show

From morning to night
Our show was in sight.
We practised for weeks
Just to get the dance right.
Young girls from three,
Teenagers and me,
Pretty costumes and make-up
And wonderful stage lights.
As the day drew closer and nearer,
We began to be clearer.
The show was great, a true success,
Mum was proud as I had done my best.

Louisa Huggins (11)
Earlham High School, Norwich

My Generation

Shop corners are the best,
Alcohol does the rest
To stop you being stressed.
As if there's hope for my generation.

Keep up with the latest craze,
Or be in a daze.
Don't forget about detention today.
Welcome to my generation.

There is no hope for an education,
Except for a select few
Who wish for a graduation.

What is the country coming to,
With all-night ravings and fast street racing?
Set some expectations!

But all I want is an explanation
As to why we can't have a calm generation!

Gemma Clark (13)
Earlham High School, Norwich

Why Are We Here?

Why are we here?
Why were we put here?
Do we live in fear of why we're here,
Do we live in fear of what we've done,
Or do we live in fear of what's to come?
Why are we here?
Why are we here?
That is the question,
It's an impossible sum.

Katie Cooney
Earlham High School, Norwich

Sad Life

A sad little girl
With a broken heart
Has a mucked-up life,
Which has torn her apart.

She has no family
To support her when she is down,
And all of her mates
Just mess her around.

Her only real friend was her boyfriend,
He didn't really care,
He dumped her for another girl,
Which turned her to despair.

She found a knife
And took her last breath.
She fell in the bath
And then drowned to death.

Natasha Parker (14)
Earlham High School, Norwich

Wendene

Dylan in goal, saving the shots,
Shane in defence has lost the plot.
Stewart in mid, catching flies,
Shawn on the sideline saying, 'Why?'
Josh in mid has lots of fights,
Nathan in the other half flying his kite.
Me up front, fast as the wind,
If I get mouthy, I'll get binned.

Dominic Dozier (12)
Earlham High School, Norwich

My Generation

My generation today,
There are many things I like
Within my generation today.
Young people nowadays have more freedom,
They have options as to what they can do.
However, you have to be cautious of what you do
In my generation today.

Everyone's generations
All have their differences.
Some are good, some are bad,
It depends on how it goes.

Other generations may be boring,
But mine is as exciting as it gets.
Every day I live as it comes,
I cherish every day with deep emotion.

Past generations,
Present generations,
Future generations,
All withhold deep secrets.

But the thing is,
You have to take life as it comes,
And that's one thing I've learnt
From my generation today.

My generation today,
There are many things I like within
My generation today.
Young people nowadays have more freedom,
They have options as to what they can do.
However, you have to be cautious of what you do
In my generation today.

Sarah Green (15)
Earlham High School, Norwich

My Generation

Teenage kids
Are in the news
Just because
Some break the rules.

With hoodies, gangs,
Yobs and thugs,
Trying to get you
Hooked on drugs.

You can say no,
It's allowed,
You don't have to be
One of the crowd.

We're not all bad,
We're not all the same,
These kind of people
Put us to shame.

Most are polite,
Some open doors,
But we do work hard,
Which deserves an applause.

Don't put us all down,
We try our best,
Please don't judge us
Just like the rest.

Laura Burroughs (15)
Earlham High School, Norwich

Why Does She Have To Leave?

I drive her to the train station,
Her suitcases are full,
She's going to Diss with her dad,
Is that all?

She's my best friend,
It's hard to believe
That she's really going.
She *has* to leave!

But why, oh why
Does this have to happen to me?
We have been best friends
Since nursery!

She's going to Diss,
But why can't she see
I love her so much?
Please don't leave!

She's pretty
And shy,
Naughty and sly,
The perfect best friend for me!

She gets on the train and we say our last goodbyes,
I give her a quick letter and it makes her cry.
'Bye Kayleigh Watts,' I say.
She'll always stay my best friend,
But *no one* will ever be better than her!

Sophie Childerhouse (12)
Earlham High School, Norwich

My New Generation

We are the new generation,
We are alike and different,
All around the nation.

If we are nice, nasty, cunning or sly,
If we want something enough,
We will always try.

We can be clever, cheeky, funny or bad,
And if we have too much sugar,
We go completely mad!

Sweets, crisps, chocolate bars,
Football, netball, but not the
Dreaded ballroom dance!

We are the new generation,
We are alike and different,
All around the nation!

Ebony Scott (13)
Earlham High School, Norwich

Love

Love is something you feel
But you can't see;
Is something special
That happens in your life *once!*

Sometimes can hurt you so much,
You feel very down
And sometimes cry.

I know many people who
Had their hearts broken because of love,
But the next day they find someone
Who loves them so much,
More than anybody else did.

Sometimes love can be hard
And very tricky,
But you never know
What could happen next.

Rute Banon (13)
Earlham High School, Norwich

Wasted Generation

People stare in the street
As I'm walking,
Looking down at my feet.

The elderly avoid me
Like there's something wrong.
The scent of wasted youth
Seems to be so strong.

But really I see nothing
That is wrong,
Just because I'm spirited,
Opinionated and strong.

Children should be
Seen and not heard.
You'd think for teenage sake
The scrutiny would be spared.

Samantha Tidd (15)
Earlham High School, Norwich

Friends

F riends are great!
R eliable mates
I can't live without my mates
E ver together
N ever leave my side
D elightful all the time
S ending love wherever we are!
We will always be together!

Kayleigh Bradley (12)
Earlham High School, Norwich

Our Generation

The fabric of our society is falling apart,
The media controls our mind, our body and now our soul.
Before, we were able to run free,
We had the ability to learn, the ability to breathe,
But this right has been swiped,
Replaced with TV, games, graphical representations of people
That may or may not care about who we are.
Forget zombie movies, we are the living dead,
We won't believe it but it's true.
Fundamentally our generation has been torn apart,
From the inside out.
The bad thing is it won't change, it can't,
Most of the time we won't want it to either,
And to me this is the saddest thing.

Keiran Womersley (16)
Earlham High School, Norwich

My Generation

DVDs, MP3s,
Computer games and Nintendo Wiis.
Emos, chavs, goths and pikeys,
Ben Sherman, Adidas, Reebok and Nike.
Fast food, junk food, fat, obese,
Nokia, Motorola, Siemens and LG.
Hip hop, rap, pop, rock,
Kanye West, Girls Aloud and Slipknot.
Million dollar CGI movies,
Bluetooth, wi-fi and flat screen TVs.
This is my generation and I'm proud,
Yes some of us are yobs that hang around in crowds,
But we are mostly decent folk, can't you see
Past our hard exteriors, attitude and hoodies?

Luke Ford (16)
Earlham High School, Norwich

Suicide

A sad girl
With a lonely life,
A broken heart
And a sharp knife.
She prayed for forgiveness
Then thought about death,
Wrote a suicide note
And took her last breath.

Ashleigh Standen (14)
Earlham High School, Norwich

Untitled

Please don't judge me by my face,
By my religion, or my race.
Please don't laugh at what I wear
Or how I look or do my hair.
It doesn't matter
Whether I look nice or not.
When I look at the mirror
I can no longer see myself.
All I can see is a lonely girl inside of me.
All I want to do is live,
Just like you all,
Want to keep my privacy inside of me.
My heart is cold as ice.
I want to stop all this,
It feels like there are too many things
Going on inside my head.
But outside there seems to be happiness.
Somehow I don't understand
Where I am, who I am
Or what I do.

Mink Goodman (13)
Hertswood School, Borehamwood

Generations

There are times when we hear a call
Calling for the world to come together
There are people dying trying
It is time to lend a hand to lives

Day by day we just can't watch people suffering,
We know that someone, somehow,
Should make a change

Let's start giving
To those whose hearts stop beating
Caused by illnesses
Let's give to other generations
Just you and me

Let them know that someone cares
We all must lend a helping hand
To those who are in need

Let us realise that a change can only come
When we stand together as one
There are choices we can make

Let's start giving
To those whose hearts stop beating
Caused by illnesses
Let's give to other generations
Just you and me.

Ratidzo Masunda (12)
Hertswood School, Borehamwood

Bliss Science

The boy with the wondering mind
Looks intangibly at the science book:
A big bang and holes in the ozone - words
And concepts inconclusively defining
The very essence of our being.

Ah, the craving for answers proves unravelling;
Quantum physics and such have no place
In his simple, honest mind. Carbon
Emissions and the like are simply the familiar
Stranger, viewed upon with some recognition, but no

Association. The boy resides inadequately from
The science book, accepting his legitimate place
And naïve conclusions. He steps outside,
Having learnt only his own insignificance in the world,
And so slowly subsides, constructing the same mistakes again.

Simon Bloomer (17)
Hitchin Boys' School, Hitchin

To The One In My Life

I can't wake from these rough dreams . . .
And as soon as I close my eyes . . .
I still hear you saying you love me . . .

You're like my rainbow just after rainfall
And you make the pain go when pain calls.
When I try to loosen your grip I'm only strained more,
So I remain in solitude wondering who you changed for,

Sometimes you forget I exist,
I still feel your lips on this cheek you kissed,
Like a coin trapped by the clench of your fist,
My heart twists with memories of when we were kids,

I'm not how I pretend to be 'cause I still look away
When you stand next to me,
It's destiny and you were sent to me,
So how can I let this love rest in peace?

The pieces of my broken heart are hard to find,
I'll still see your face in the stars tonight,
I put on this front, acting like I could leave your side
But, walking away from you is like leaving myself behind.

You don't listen to the points I make here
And you don't dry my eyes when they break tears,
These feelings won't disappear,
So I put on this act like Shakespeare,

As much as I want you to be erased,
A love like yours can't be replaced,
When I look at other girls I only see your face,
Why can't you feel my tears on your skin when we embrace?

Maybe it's your loss, but I'm the one
That's losing my mind in this confusion,
My heart won't protect me from your intrusions,
So I'm stuck chasing this illusion.

You would pick me up when I was crying about things
So being happy and not with you
Is like flying without wings,
And I feel like a chain without a link -
A winter without rain, or a yang without ying,

I need this more than I want this,
With my head in my hands, I still picture that one kiss,
In this world there's no justice 'cause
You won't find another love like mine - that's a promise,

No lie . . . you're the only one in my mind
But it seems I'm the only one in this fight,
You're all I want in my life . . .
I dedicate this to the one in my life . . .

Priyan Odedra (15)
Ilford County High School, Ilford

Cars

Coming on back like a racing Nova
When you're winning it feels like it's over
Running smooth on the low Bridgestones
When you're racing you feel you're alone
When you step on the gas
Make the nitrous blast
Put the pedal to the metal
Leave rivals in the past

Rolling on twenty-one inch rims
Driving along in my flaming skins
400 watts of blasting power
Travelling at 200 miles per hour
I begin to turn up the heat
With my girl in the passenger seat
500 horsepower down the hill
I slam the brakes to a standstill.

Christian Goddard (15)
Integrated Support Service, Harlow

You Succeeded

If it was your plan to make me detest myself
Then well done
You succeeded

If your dream was to make me paranoid and depressed
It took some time
But you succeeded

If you wanted nothing more than to see me fail
Give yourself a pat on the back
Cos you succeeded

If you wanted me to blame myself for your mistakes
Then you achieved your goal
And you succeeded

If your ambition was to make me maim my arms
Then you worked hard
Cos you succeeded

You must have been desperate to make me scared but violent
Cos it took you fifteen years
But you succeeded

If you wanted me to worry constantly for my sisters
Woman you don't give up
You succeeded

If you were eager to beat me and make me homeless
Your persistence paid off
And you succeeded

If you wanted me to feel lonely and guilty
Then order the champagne
You succeeded

If you wanted to ruin me and make me hate you more
than anything
Then don't worry
You succeeded.

Sarah Graham (15)
Integrated Support Service, Harlow

My World Of Equality

My life, my story,
My generation,
The strength, the will and the patience,
What should I do?
What would I do
To make this world my dream come true?
No hate, no distress, no famine, no plague,
No war, no hatred, no slave,
No matter of colour, no matter of religion,
Just be fair to all, that's my decision.
I wish that people wouldn't care
What you look like or what you wear.
I wish that people wouldn't read the articles in the magazines
About being amazingly skinny or clinically obese.
I wish that people could be free and happy
Living in peace and equality.

Emily Vinson (13)
Ixworth Middle School, Bury St Edmunds

The Opposites Of Life

Rich and famous
With bags of money.
Poor and homeless with
Nothing but a pot of honey.

Posh children beaming
With the latest computer game.
Others standing at the side
Dreaming if they could be that cool.

People having dinner parties
With lovely dresses and yummy food.
Families having to scavenge for
Half-eaten food with their stomachs rumbling.

Why should there be two sides of life,
Cut in half with a knife?
We should all be one, together forever
With no one left out because we all
Should have a right to a good life.

Lucy Reader (12)
Ixworth Middle School, Bury St Edmunds

Imagine

Imagine a world with no wars,
No injuries, no blood, no fights.
A world of kindness,
Full of peaceful sights.

Imagine a world with no poverty,
Where every child gets food to eat.
Everyone has a right to education,
A home to live in, not on the street.

Imagine a world with no AIDS.
For every person to access medical care.
Cures for illnesses that kill.
Now this is what would be fair.

Imagine a world with less waste,
Less pollution and no global warming.
A world that recycles their rubbish.
This really would be transforming.

Imagine a world where everyone is treated the same,
Whatever religion, and colour their skin or hair.
A world with friendly people.
This would stop so much despair.

Imagine a world with no crime and abuse.
A world of freedom to be who you want to be,
Where every person feels safe and secure.
A vision that everyone can see.

Imagine a world with all of this.
A world of happiness and hope,
Full of opportunities.
Just imagine . . .

Rebecca Laidlaw (13)
Ixworth Middle School, Bury St Edmunds

One Day Of Happiness, That's All I Ask

Today's youth are not constantly depressed,
We just are victims of the issues of our generation.

World issues like poverty and global warming,
Oil shortage and animal testing,
Unfair distribution of money;
And worst of all, war.

Family issues like parents splitting up
Or people being ill; people dying
Or being poor.

School issues like hard homework or failing a test,
Being bullied, that's not rare.

All are issues of this generation,
Everyone wishes things could change,
If only for one day, these things could rearrange.

One wish could change this,
No one would be depressed on that day,
Everyone would love and keep the peace,
No one would harm another being, wahey!
And no one would argue,
No one would fight,
Everyone would love with all of their might.

If only that day was real, not just my dream,
One day of true happiness I'd like to see,
No one would argue,
No one would fight
And just for one day it would all be all right.

Just for one day if these things could transform
Nobody would mourn,
And if there was no pain,
Then people could truly love and be happy again.

Jasmine Rutterford (13)
Ixworth Middle School, Bury St Edmunds

That's My Generation!

Talking 'n' texting,
'N' moaning 'n' groaning,
That's my generation.
Skinny thin or super fat,
Pizza, kebabs, chips 'n' that.
This is my generation.
Drugs 'n' fags,
Shoes 'n' bags,
That's my generation.
Money 'n' debts,
To buy or to let,
That's my generation.
Global warming,
Mum 'n' Dad ignoring,
That's my generation.
Nintendos 'n' iPods,
Lack of whales 'n' cod,
That's my generation.
Will my generation
Be the last generation?

Abbey Kurton (13)
Ixworth Middle School, Bury St Edmunds

What's The Point In Living?

What's the point in living
If we can't have our say?
Each and every person
Living a rule restricted day.

The saying 'It's a free country'
Is frequently tossed around,
It is saying we can do what we please,
When in fact we are all legally bound.

Children to education,
Pressure piled on each day.
Adults to work,
But they do get paid.

The government rules over us,
We obey what they teach,
But the question is,
Do they practise what they preach?

Still we have our own private space,
A place that's full of laughter -
It's surely better shared,
So spread a little kindness
To show people that you care.

Kirstie Wright (13)
Ixworth Middle School, Bury St Edmunds

Memory

In the eyes of my memory
What can I see?
A girl by herself,
Books on the shelf.

Her friends are outside
But she had to hide,
She didn't cry,
Her mum knows why.

Wanted to tell school,
Felt like a fool.
All in my memory
When I got stuck in a tree.

Friends all chuckled
When I fell in a puddle,
I'm not the only one
Who's been and done . . .

Why did she do that?
Wear a lampshade hat.
Didn't mean to fall over,
I need a four-leaf clover.

In the eyes of my memory
What can I see?
A girl by herself,
Books on the shelf.

Lucy Tatum (11)
Long Stratton High School, Long Stratton

We Are The Foxes

I am the urban fox,
This city's my home,
Where headlights flash
And storm clouds crash,
I am the urban fox.

I am the rural fox,
This woodland is my home,
Where songbirds sing
And church bells ring,
I am the rural fox.

I am the urban fox,
If I am in the mood
I forage for my food,
I sleep upon a dustbin,
I am the urban fox.

I am the rural fox,
I sleep cosy in my den,
I catch my prey in my paws
And take it in my deadly jaws,
I am the rural fox.

We are the foxes
Of countryside and city,
We live completely different lives,
From cosy dens and fresh full meals
To draughty dustbins and little scraps,
We are the foxes
And we are proud.

Claudia St Quintin (12)
Long Stratton High School, Long Stratton

Through The Eyes Of A Kitten

Through the eyes of a tiny kitten
I saw a little mouse inside a little mitten,
He nibbled cheese and sang happy songs,
So all the other mice could hear him,
So I chased him round the kitchen,
He squealed and squirmed
When I was on his thin pink tail,
But he escaped through my nimble paws
And went through one of the doors.
I hissed and ran after him with my sharp claws,
'Where are you, you little mouse?'
Ha! Found you Mousey!
The mouse scrambled into his hole,
I pushed my fluffy paw through
The dark little hole he had made.
'Ha! I've caught you now, you grey fluff ball!'
Scrap, scrap, scrap!
Now you're dead, you tiny mouse,
Time for me to gobble you all up.
Gulp! That was the best meal I have had in months.
Yummy!

Chloe Scott (11)
Long Stratton High School, Long Stratton

No

My generation is all about violence and wars
Guns and knives some people must have
Police say *no,* these things must go

My generation is all about the web
How fun it is but how dangerous it can be
Parents say *no,* these computers must go

My generation, everyone wants to be famous
On the X Factor they all go
The judges say *no,* these people must go.

Chrystal Hendry (12)
Lonsdale School, Stevenage

Never Boring

The brave me
Hops down the
Beautiful hall

In my bright
Silver jacket
How posh!

At my
Hot bird's
Old place!

2am in
The morn
Yeah!

My generation.
Bold, brave,
But never boring!

Danny Blake (11)
Lonsdale School, Stevenage

My Generation

Queen Elizabeth
Holds head high while strolling
Through her royal house
Metres from her jewels
Waiting to meet her people
That's my generation.

Becky Goodwill (12)
Lonsdale School, Stevenage

The History Of Politics

(To the tune of 'Miss Molly had a Dolly')

In nineteen-forty, Winston Churchill's in.
In World War II he helped us win.
Everybody thought he would walk right in,
But in nineteen forty-five, Clement Atlee did grin.

After term one, he won again.
Then Winston Churchill, Sir before his name.
Anthony Eden, he was a pain,
He attacked Egypt for a monetary gain.

Harold Macmillan should have taken better care.
His minister of war was having an affair.
That was what led to his doom.
Next in line, Sir Alec Douglas Home.

Harold Wilson is the next you see,
From sixty-four to nineteen-seventy.
Then Edward Heath, the prime minister who
Dragged Great Britain into the EU.

Harold Wilson, such a sneaky man,
He won again with a sneaky plan.
James Callaghan was as thick as can be,
As he never bothered with university.

Next was the 'Iron Lady', Margaret Thatcher,
For three terms no politician could catch her.
She led the world and she led our state,
Until she was betrayed and then replaced.

John Major for seven years, almost eight,
And Tony Blair, he beat his mate.
His mate Gordon Brown, we all say,
Is the prime minister of today.

Benjamin Ely (17)
Luton Sixth Form College, Luton

Fairy Tale

There once was a little girl
Who had only one curl,
Her name was Leah,
She was so small you could hardly see her.
Yet her heart was so great,
Full of love and not hate,
For her poor lovely mum,
Who ended her day in the wolf's hungry tum.

Many years later,
When she had grown so much greater,
She was walking in the woods
With her brother, Robin Hood,
When she spied the wolf so hairy
And devilishly scary.
Her brother ran away
But she decided to stay
To kill the grey beast
Who had made such a feast
Of her mother so fair,
With lovely straight hair.
She crouched down low
And took out a bow
And killed him stone dead
With an arrow in the head.

She went to her gran's
And clasped her old hands,
Without missing a beat,
She told of her feat
Of killing the animal
That was such a cannibal,
And they all danced with laughter
And lived happily ever after.

Charlotte Pothecary (13)
Margaret Beaufort Middle School, Bedford

Poppy War

Poppies don't mean red petals,
Poppies mean red blood.

Poppies are not beautiful,
Poppies are muddy trenches.

Poppies don't mean happiness,
Poppies mean sadness.

Poppies are not cheerful,
Poppies are suffering and pain.

Poppies don't mean fresh air,
Poppies mean drowning in gas.

Poppies are not comfort,
Poppies are a death bed.

Poppies don't mean cured forever,
Poppies mean scarred for life.

Poppies . . . show war
War . . . shouldn't be!

Sarah Nash (13)
Margaret Beaufort Middle School, Bedford

Dawn Of War

Bang! is the sound of machine guns.
We have cuts, bruises and burst eardrums.
When they go over the top
We can only hope the bombs will stop.

It comes our turn and we push them back,
After all of that, my mind's lost track,
And we take them back to the shore.
We can only wait for the dawn of war.

James Langley (13)
Margaret Beaufort Middle School, Bedford

War Is

War is not glory
War is death

War is not fun
War is like someone losing their child

War is not a red rose
War is blood shedding

War is not children having fun
War is children running away

War is not a happy ending
War is a happily never after

War is not a flower
War is a poppy in remembrance of death

War is . . .*wrong*
And I believe it should die forever.

Luke Pidgeon (12)
Margaret Beaufort Middle School, Bedford

Warning

When I am an old woman, I shall
Wear a bin bag to dress up for a party,
Flirt with young guys and act all tarty.
Grow fat on my belly and lay about.
Stand in the rain and start to shout.
Wear a bikini to the village shop,
Become all tough and challenge a cop.

But while I am young I shall
Listen to my mum,
Eat my veg and fruit,
Listen to the old
And wear a pretty suit.

Tilly Gardner (12)
Margaret Beaufort Middle School, Bedford

Lorna Beauty

The king and queen had just one daughter,
The rest of them were done and slaughtered.
'But this time my beautiful baby girl
Will not be touched, not even her curls.'
The queen clutched her darling baby
But then her smile quickly faded.
A terrible witch dressed in black
Was standing behind Lorna's back.
The woman watched with hateful eyes
A baby dreaming of birds that fly.
She clenched her fists then waved her hand
And Lorna woke and could not stand.
'Little Lorna, you awful fiend,
Will be punished with a sewing machine!'
Everyone gasped, Lorna cried,
'I will not let my baby die!'
The king and queen locked all rooms,
So not even a flower could bloom.
The years went by, Lorna was lovely,
She wanted a prince who was bright and bubbly,
But then one day she got a letter,
It made her feel an awful lot better!
The prince was coming, she'd better get dressed,
He'd change his mind if she's in a mess!
She rushed to her room and then she found
An old woman sitting on the ground.
'Well hello, my dearest Lorna lovely,
I'll make a dress that's bright and bubbly.'
Lorna was not stupid, she wasn't a fool,
She had to stop her once and for all.
'I'm not falling for that, you evil witch,
I could sense your lies and I saw you twitch!'
With that, the woman was dead on the floor.
'I really don't need him anymore!'

Lorna skipped off, all perfect and sweet,
But then the prince was at her feet.
'Away with you, I'm a strong Princess,
I don't care if I'm a mess.'

Lucy Hoogstraten (13)
Margaret Beaufort Middle School, Bedford

War

War is not a game,
War is excruciating pain.

War is not a red poppy,
War is a red stream of blood.

War is not a sweet dream,
War is sour reality.

War is not happy and fun,
War is brutal death.

War is not fun,
It's destruction.

War is not open fields,
War is black over light over fields.

War is not a glorious death,
War is a painful death.

War is not glory,
War is painful and gory.

Sanjeev Bains (12)
Margaret Beaufort Middle School, Bedford

War Is Glorious?

The glory of war,
Getting smashed by a bomb.

The glory of war,
Getting slaughtered by a man you don't know.

The glory of war,
Getting your head blown off by a grenade.

The glory of war,
Living with rats.

The glory of war,
Sleepless nights, thinking of the death of tomorrow.

The glory of war,
There's no restart button.

The glory of war,
Watching your friend die, right in front of your eyes.

The glory of war,
What glory of war?

Jack Freeman (13)
Margaret Beaufort Middle School, Bedford

What Is War?

Red isn't the colour of grass,
Red isn't the colour of sky,
Red is the colour of blood,
Blood isn't just red,
Blood isn't just a cut,
Blood is death,
Death isn't a year in jail,
Death isn't a cut of the knee,
Death is the end of Man.

Jack Boakes (12)
Margaret Beaufort Middle School, Bedford

Warning

When I am old I shall wear knee-high stockings and shawls,
Ridiculous flowery skirts and shirts,
Shoes the colour of cement walls,
And shoes that when I walk, hurt.

When I am old I shall look awful,
My grandchildren will be embarrassed to see me.
They shall say, 'Grandma, is that lawful?'
And I will say, 'Ah! We shall see!'

When I am old I shall eat jam cakes and tarts,
And cheese and bread,
And apples loaded in carts,
And medicine that tastes like lead.

When I am old I shall bake,
There will be mountains and mountains of cake.
I will bake things it's not possible to make
And all my food you shall want to take.

When I'm old I shall think young people are silly,
They are all so dreadfully skinny.
I'll tell them, 'Fatten up or outside will seem chilly!'
And they will say, 'Don't be a ninny!'

When I'm old I shall have lots of strange habits,
Like going to get my milk in my nightgown and slippers.
I'll have a weird obsession with rabbits
And I shall be afraid of flippers.

Each day I shall go to bingo,
We'll play all the Beatles' songs there.
We shall talk about Paul McCartney and Ringo,
And I'll go to sewing groups to stitch up one tear.

Each day I shall go to tea and coffee mornings,
And gobble up home-made gingerbread men.
I'll sell my famous cakes (with walnut warnings),
And leave, but I'll never know when!

Nicola Carter (12)
Margaret Beaufort Middle School, Bedford

Is War Right Or Is War Wrong?

Is war right
Or is war wrong?

Is war glory
Or is war death?

Is war beautiful
Or is war dirt?

Is war bright
Or is war dull?

Is war fun
Or is war fear?

Is war a flower
Or is war mud?

Is war lovely
Or is war ghastly?

Is war flowing water
Or is war flowing blood?

Is war right
Or is war wrong?

Robert Parker (12)
Margaret Beaufort Middle School, Bedford

War

W ar is horrible,
A nd not a way of life,
R ats and misery everywhere.

I s this your way of life?
S uffering every day, waiting to die?

D ark and cold, night after night,
E very day, torture and death,
A nd not a way of life,
T orture, torture, torture,
H orrible to the end.

Y ou may get diseased,
O r maybe even injured,
U se your mind to think.

W hy?
I njured you may be,
L icking your wounds like an injured dog,
L iving in pain.

D o you want this life?
I don't think so,
E nd all wars!

Ben Sharp (12)
Margaret Beaufort Middle School, Bedford

War Is . . .

War is not a glorious dream
War is a horrible nightmare

War is not like a game where you can restart
War is a one chance ending

War is not birds flying through the sky
War is a plane flying, dropping bombs

War is not play, pretend guns and fighting
War is the real thing

War is not a happy day with your family
War is a sad death with your friends

War is not looking after your children
War is sending innocent children to die

War is not a road to victory
War is a long, dark, twisting road to death

War is not your finest hour
War is your darkest hours

War is not a nice warm glass of red wine
War is a spill of red, bitter blood

War is not a nice drive out in the car
War is a bumpy and dangerous drive in a tank

War is a terrible thing.

Alex Jafarifar (13)
Margaret Beaufort Middle School, Bedford

Fairy Tale

Once upon a time a small princess was born,
A fairy came to the christening and with an evil scorn
She said, 'This princess will be cursed forever,
When she turns eighteen and cuts her hand on a shaver
She will sleep for a hundred years and never wake.'
And with that she left with a huge earthquake.
Then came a good fairy and with a swish
She granted the baby just one wish.
As the baby couldn't speak, the king and queen
Decided to make it for her.
So they thought and thought and came up with this,
Maybe a prince will give her a kiss
And then she will wake up and without a miss,
She will marry him on the spot,
That should do it, a perfect snapshot.
So they waited and waited till the day finally came,
When poor Elizabeth (for that was her name)
Was shaving her legs when she cut her hand,
She fell asleep, she was dead to the land.
A prince came riding down the street,
His dream princess he wanted to meet.
He opened the door
And saw her lying on the floor.
He bent down to kiss her, but as he bent down,
He shot back up and rode back to the town.
As he left, he shouted to the queen,
'I'm not kissing that, it needs a good clean!'

Prudence Wady (13)
Margaret Beaufort Middle School, Bedford

Warning

When I grow old I will:
Ride a BMX on the skate park,
Wearing a pink fluorescent hat,
And rollerblade down to my local
And drink lemonade while I chat.

When I grow old I will:
Eat pizza and popcorn and jelly with cream,
While sitting and watching a movie.
For pudding I'll eat a banana
'Cause this always makes me feel groovy.

When I grow old I will:
Wear a bright purple dress and shiny red shoes
And a big fluffy hat with a bow,
Then I'll walk down the street in my lime-green coat
And parade round the town really slow.

Every day I will go to Blackpool
And travel first class on the train.
I will always have tea with my neighbour,
'Cause she's lovely but can be a pain.

Chris Bishop (11)
Margaret Beaufort Middle School, Bedford

War!

War is like a cloudy puddle,
War is unlike a summer's morning.
War is like a crazy muddle,
War is unlike the sunrise dawning.

War is like a deep, dark hole,
War is unlike a sunny countryside.
War is like flowers being replaced with coal,
War is unlike a funfair slide.

War is like the woods at night,
War is unlike a family holiday.
War is like it being dark with no light,
War is unlike watching kids play.

War is like a firework display,
War is unlike a banquet feast.
War is like everybody in dismay,
War is unlike Beauty and the Beast.

War is like thunder and lightning,
War is unlike a bunch of red roses.
War is like a film that's frightening,
War is unlike ogling a baby while it dozes.

Hayley Louise Gibson (13)
Margaret Beaufort Middle School, Bedford

Warning For When I'm Old

When I am old
I will not do as I am told,
I will learn new things
As I am not blamed for my actions,
My age is . . .

When I am old,
And don't do as I am told,
I will wear bright clothes,
All the colours of the rainbow,
And a little headband with the peace sign on it.

When I am old
And I don't do as I am told,
I will eat porridge for breakfast,
With my bread and chilli for lunch
And thirty jam sandwiches for dinner.

When I am old
And I don't do as I am told,
I will think young people are dull,
And sensible,
When they are setting examples.

When I am old
And I don't do as I am told,
I will collect a jar of chicken claws,
I will collect it at the chicken factory
And nibble on some when I am hungry.

When I am old
And I don't do what I am told,
I will live in the Melchbourne Wood
In a little tepee.
With a llama.

When I am old
And I don't do as I am told,
Each day after breakfast I will go to the Riseley brook,
And go swimming in the nude.
At 3.30 I will cycle on my tricycle to Riseley Park,
Greet the children from the lower school
And tell them to push me on the swing.

When I am old
And I don't do as I am told,
I will be wacky,
With my llama, Frederick.

Olivia Greco (11)
Margaret Beaufort Middle School, Bedford

My War Poem

War is not glory,
War is shameful.

War is not a poppy in a field,
War is a field full of blood.

War is not pure beef,
War is beef in a can.

War is not happy and fun,
War is sad and glum.

War is not trying to survive,
War is dying.

War is not coming home,
War is coming home in a coffin.

War is not good,
War is bad.

Jedd Hallett (12)
Margaret Beaufort Middle School, Bedford

Warning

When I am old I will wear rainbow-coloured suspenders
With bright T-shirts,
With my father's old woolly socks pulled up above my ankles,
An odd pair of course,
And a wig of grey curly hair,
With radically thick glasses and use phrases like
'Groovy baby' and *'Shasam!'*
I will spend all my money on gym lessons and instruments.
At night, I will feast on all apricots and ugly fruits
With sugar apples at the side,
With melted ice cream to wash it all away.
And even after all that, I will never brush my teeth.
I will speak two languages for different audiences:
For guests, English, for friends and family, Bad English.
I will hate young people with their boring lives,
Living like robots with the rules, the responsibilities,
The pressure and the good behaviour.
I will collect people's toenail clippings and old newspapers
And do cartwheels along the streets and not care who I hit.
I will lie down on the pavement to just look at the sky.
Each day I will go to a circus and ask to join it
And perform on that day.

Maybe I should be like that now?
Live for the moment
Or wait till later on?

Rebecca Franklin (12)
Margaret Beaufort Middle School, Bedford

Warning

When I am old I will wear flat, colourless shoes
And a summer dress in all the seasons,
Perhaps changing the dull colour.

When I am old I will eat roasts every Sunday,
Child's meals, i.e. fish fingers
Every other day of the week.

When I am old I will poke people with my walking stick,
I don't care what others think
I've been a wild one all my life.

I will think that young people
Are little monsters,
Noisy and atrocious,
But I will forgive them
Knowing I once was one.

My habits will be strange,
No doubt about that.
What will happen to me?
Well, will I go nuts?
What are my habits?
Well I will decide,
It could be
Getting help for no reason,
Whatever the season.
I will be cheeky
But no one will suspect.

Molly Ziemelis (12)
Margaret Beaufort Middle School, Bedford

Freedom

When I'm old, there's no rules for me,
Dancing and prancing, filled with glee.
Eating dessert before the main course
And galloping around the field on a big horse.
Rotting my false teeth with sweets,
I won't make my bed; no cover or sheets.

I will waste all my pension money,
Then watch 'You've Been Framed', it's really quite funny!
I will go out for a morning hunt,
Then turn on the radio and listen to James Blunt.
I could sleep all day,
I don't care what you say.

I will wear odd gloves and socks
And I won't bother with clocks.
I will sing all night
And give the neighbours a fright.
So don't fear getting old,
Your life isn't on hold.

Ian Yarwood (11)
Margaret Beaufort Middle School, Bedford

Holiday Memories

I can see the grey clouds,
I can touch my umbrella,
I feel the biting rain,
I am thinking, *I hate the British weather.*
I can hear the screeching seagulls,
I can smell something bad,
I can taste the salty air,
I am saying, 'Why didn't we go to Spain?'

But wait!

I can see the clouds clearing,
I can touch the warm sand,
I feel the rays of sun,
I am thinking, *the sun's out at last.*
I can hear the laughing children,
I can taste the candyfloss,
I can smell the suntan lotion,
I am singing, 'Oh I do like to be beside the seaside'!

James Holyoake (12)
Margaret Beaufort Middle School, Bedford

When The School Bell Rings

It echoes across the playground.
It echoes over the fields beyond.
It echoes across the seas and makes the Earth shimmer.
The school bell rings four times each day,
The first at the start of school.
You stomp to your classroom and slump down into your seat.
The teacher drones on and on.
English.
Mathematics,
All are boring.
Then you hear it echo.
The school bell rings.
It is now lunch, the best time of the day.
You race out onto the fields, wishing you could do it all day.
The lunches are sloppy and gooey though,
They dump stuff on your plate which you do not want.
The whole class stays behind until you have finished your meal,
Then the school bell rings again.
Ring, ring, ring,
'Time for afternoon' it says.
You stomp to your class and slump down into your seat,
The teacher drones on and on.
Science,
RE,
History,
Ring, ring, ring,
The school bell sounds.
The children laugh and play
Because it's the end of the school day.

Jacob Collins (12)
New Hall School, Chelmsford

Living Senseless

I used to be the only one who had never tried any at fifteen.
'Just one drink,' she said, 'will do you no harm.'
There was no reason for me not to.
The vodka went in, then came back out.
Step 1. Became a part of the group.

I never really stole from anyone, maybe my sisters.
'The old bat down the road won't be in tonight.'
There was no reason for me not to.
An expensive radio gift for my mum.
Step 2. Became second in command.

No one really cared about the local shop.
'It's only owned by the Robinsons.'
There was no reason for me not to.
We sprayed the 'skull',
The symbol of the gang.
Step 3. Became the leader of the group.

I don't know where he got it from.
'A few sniffs won't do us no damage.'
There was no reason for me not to.
One sniff I did, I couldn't feel my face,
The cocaine felt good, sending electricity through me.
Step 4. Got caught by the old bill.

I tried to hit the incredibly strong blue bottle.
'Calm down love! The station's only ten minutes away!'
So now here I am, ten years in the slam,
For something I could have avoided.
Step 5. Realised what I had missed before . . .

All those reasons that told me not to.

Sophia Miller de Vega (14)
New Hall School, Chelmsford

Breath To Death

I can feel it fester inside me, I don't know what, but it's there.
The Devil, a spirit that eats my flesh away and away,
Until it happens. My friends offered me something the other day
But I declined. Though I think I've changed my mind.

I've always been taught to respect my elders and put up
with them.

At school I'm told to look after the environment,
Clean up the mess they made. They. I didn't make it, why
should I help?
It's their problem, and I'll be gone before long.

I hate the stereotypes that plague me every day, from the old,
They think they know everything,
But they can't even tell the difference between fresh
and mouldy,
Who do they think they are? I hate them.

But I'm going to forget all of this now, my time has come.
No one wants me anymore, no one!
I walk into my dad's workshop, grab the rope and map.
I take a knife just in case, as well.

I find a derelict school, a memorable place for me, ha.
I find a rusty pole sticking out of the wall
And tie the rope in a noose. It goes round my neck.
My last breath.
At last, death.

Daniel Mullens (13)
New Hall School, Chelmsford

Talkin' 'Bout My Generation

Be responsible, that's what they say,
But for what and why?
There is no special book explaining things, just us,
And maybe we don't know how,
Maybe we mess things up because that is what we have to do,
Perhaps no one ever realised that being responsible
takes something,
Something unknown to Man.

Responsibility, that is what *that* generation have to understand,
Self-control and when to say *no*.
They really need to learn
It brings tears to my eyes and makes me bow my head in
shame and pity.

Why can't it be how it used to be,
A quiet safe life in the country?
But now, one step out of line
And you will be punished.

We try,
Sometimes we don't succeed,
People just don't understand.
They were young once,
They know what it feels like,
To feel free,
To feel that you are invincible.
Maybe they just care,
Care for us,
Like we will do for our children.
Overprotection . . .
That is the reason for this.

Eleanor Kibblewhite (11)
New Hall School, Chelmsford

Talking 'Bout My Generation

A generation of fear
Is how I may choose to describe the world I live in,
On edge,
Always,
A knife edge,
The knife that separates us from you,
Cutting *us* up inside,
Bearing the blame on us.
But who should really take the fall?
Fearing a generation
You created.

You.

We may be the ones out there,
But who puts us there in the first place?
Certainly wasn't ourselves.

So who made the first cut?

Lauren Sudders (13)
New Hall School, Chelmsford

Regret

Before I was pretty,
Now my face is mouldy and rotting away.
I used to be smart,
Now the only thing on my mind is a pile of dirt.
I was always generous,
Now the only thing I give is flesh and bone.
God set out my life but I cleared the page.
Why did I do it?
Sometimes I wonder the same thing.
My parents had to see their little girl
Lowered into an early grave,
And I chose my fate.
No one forced me, I was the one that tied the rope
And I was the one that wrote the letter.
My life was not that bad,
Much better than the fate that awaited me,
Deep and utter regret.

Abigail Odell (14)
New Hall School, Chelmsford

What's In Our Hands?

Can you hear people say that it's in our hands?
But what is in our hands?
The future? The world? What?
Some older people say that we are small and dumb
And others, well they turn up their noses and try
To harm us, to cheat us, to scare us,
Just because they are bigger than us and because they can.
When we reach a certain age we are expected to
Work hard, have good grades, never disobey our elders,
But we're only children after all.
What did our parents do?
I'm sure they were not as good as they say.
I know they are trying to look after us
But it can all get too much.
People label others as black, white, popular, nerds.
But why?
You work your way to the top at primary,
And then you are small, timid and alone.
No one cares, no one knows.
In our world that we've destroyed,
We live and try to fix.
It is all put on our shoulders,
But we're only children after all.

Sophie Thompson-Hyland (12)
New Hall School, Chelmsford

Shakespearean Fun

Boil 'n' bubble, foil 'n' doom,
The witch had no clothes on and fell off her broom.
Boil 'n' bubble, foil 'n' fee,
Knights took off their armour and drank some tea.

Bubble 'n' boil, foil 'n' fie,
Prospero surrendered and started to cry.
Bubble 'n' boil, foil 'n' fun,
The king resigned and started to run.

Boil 'n' foil, fie 'n' bubble,
Guards threw down their spears and created some trouble.
Boil 'n' foil, fie 'n' tiff,
The barons ate beans and then out came the whiff.

Boil 'n' foil, bubble 'n' horde,
The priest threw down his hat and declared, 'I am bored.'
Boil 'n' bubble, foil 'n' foe,
The witches imprisoned some men and chopped off their toes.

Boil 'n' bubble, foil 'n' fie,
Now it's time to say goodbye.
Boil 'n' bubble, foil 'n' tum,
I hope you have had Shakespearean fun!

Edward Judd (13)
Richard Hale School, Hertford

A Wood Full Of Souls

Darkness flows across the wood
Shattering life like a witch's hood
In the coldness trees look bare
But the wood souls are waiting there

Swooping low and swooping high
Wood full souls come out to spy

And as the wood seems all so calm,
It interests a boy from the farm
He's heard tales of death and of woe
But he's come this far and so he goes

Swooping low and swooping high
Wood full souls come out to spy

He travels the road oh so very slow
Dazed of death that is about to show
He whispers slowing, 'What is this?'
The souls of the wood wail and hiss

Swooping low and swooping high
Wood full souls come out to spy

He screams of terror and of fright
As the wood souls come to his sight
The howling wind whips and cries
The wood full souls swarm and fly

Swooping low and swooping high
Wood full souls come out to spy

The black-hearted trees sway and rock
To capture the boy in a deadly lock
And as the souls fly up so high
They pierce the boy and leave him to die

Swooping low and swooping high
Wood full souls come out to spy.

Chris Anelay (12)
Richard Hale School, Hertford

I'm Not Here Yet

Cowgirl, a pose only the greatest can pull off,
Tassels hanging from your arm, plastic gun within your palm,
Pointing at the camera, the bandit.
Curvy hat covering your scalp at an angle
And the sign of a scruff neck, the bandana,
The symbol of your group. . .
But where is your horse, trusty steed, stallion?
Oh well, resting I guess.
Yeehaa, a young Annie Oakley.
I'm not yours, I'm not yours, I'm not yours.

Ouch! Painful, it must be that new haircut,
Hmm, straight then curls bobbing at the bottom,
Wipe that grin off your face, sitting in your living room,
White cast around your wrist, silly teenager,
Gran said you fell down the stairs, I chuckled,
But you have not thought of me yet, have you?
I'm still within the mist of the air.
I'm still not yours, I'm still not yours, I'm still not yours.

Only five years have passed,
Crawling along the duvet, bed bug in action.
You got me a Power Ranger suit, white, my favourite.
Wrapping me up in a white towel,
Singing 'Truly Scrumptious' in my ear again.
I see you on the phone talking to a friend,
You laugh and smile, I smile at your joy,
I don't know what is happening, only that it is good.
I am yours, I am yours, I am yours.

Sizzle, drip, pop. Cooking in the kitchen, licking the bowl,
Cake mixture all over my mouth, yum, good job Mum.
Later in time I am writing a poem about you,
All the good things in life we have done together.
Mother and son. Love with love.
I'm not yours, I'm not yours . . . you are mine.

Sam Stewart (15)
Richard Hale School, Hertford

First Day Of School

It was my very first day of school
I felt very uncool
As I walked through the gates
I looked for some mates
And then went the school bell

On my very first day of school

I met my new teacher, Mrs Besson
She said it was time for a lesson
So I sat in my seat
But had to sit near a cheat
And now he steals all my answers

On my very first day of school

I began to get annoyed
And now school cannot be enjoyed
Every time he speaks
He takes a little peek
Now I really am starting to boil over

On my very first day of school

It is now time for our tests
And I will be trying my very best
But he now has cheated again
It is now making me insane
And I may find myself in expulsion

On my very first day of school

I told the Head what's going on
And how he was being a con
He said he'd take care of it
And told the cheater to sit
And now school is a breeze.

Luke Thompson (13)
Richard Hale School, Hertford

Nine Eleven

This started off as an ordinary day
But would end in no ordinary way
It was just a day at work
Round the corner death did lurk
On the day of nine eleven
Lots of people went to Heaven.

On this day in New York
There was no warning to abort
With over 100 storeys high
A plane crashed into it through the sky
On the day of nine eleven
Lots of people went to Heaven.

As the towers came crashing down
It did cause more than a frown
It hurt everyone around the globe
Not many people could cope
On the day of nine eleven
Lots of people went to Heaven.

It was caused by horrible men
Questions asked - what, why and when?
A plan was made for no reason
Must be worse than committing treason
On the day of nine eleven
Lots of people went to Heaven.

Could be classed as the world's worst day
Just four months after May
Seven years on and still no clues
Why there were bombs in their shoes
On the day of nine eleven
Lots of people went to Heaven.

Harry Jones (13)
Richard Hale School, Hertford

The Six-Day War Ballad

As Israeli forces prepared to fight
The United States took sympathy on their plight
As support came it offered a spectacular sight
For the US weapons were about to show their might.
As battle loomed ahead
As gunfire shook the land
US weapons were offering a helping hand
Used on the heat of the desert sand
Victory now looked very close

Rockets illuminated the night sky
Those that were hit going to die
A single soldier being hit in the thigh
The sand was no longer going to be dry
As the blood of enemies littered the battlefield
Enemy troops had now retreated
Their routed armies now depleted
For Israel now had not been defeated
Victory was very close

At the end of the fighting new territory was gained
With enemy forces being all but maimed
While their leaders were humiliated and shamed
Their subordinates trying not to be blamed
As their armies were now defeated
The victors now shone with pride
The enemy troops in the desert lied
New territory gained the distance between the Mersey
and Clyde
Victory had now come.

Henry Bedford (13)
Richard Hale School, Hertford

The Flying Watering Can

There was a magic watering can,
It had a friend, cooking pan,
Inside it lived an old moth,
I blew into it and took off
And went round and round the world.

I took it to my house,
Where I found a tiny mouse,
It ran into its hole as I walked through the door,
I put the watering can next to my stuffed boar,
The mouse put its head out of its hole
And through the floor came a mole.

My house was old,
I had trouble with moles,
They came in swarms
As they liked the warmth,
But not the cold.

I tried it out again today,
I went off and away,
But when I tried to go back down,
The way to do it could not be found,
I tried and tried but was overtaken by a fly.

I tried the opposite
And went to find somewhere to sit
I sucked and sucked and went inside,
You'll never guess what I was going to find,
Now I'm stuck here for all time.

Matthew Hayes (12)
Richard Hale School, Hertford

The Pub

A man went into a pub (ha ha)
But this is no joke, he had travelled far
'Give me a beer and I'll tell you my tale
Travelling over mountain and vale.

In John O'Groats my journey began
And this pub is at the end of land,
For I have heard this pub is the best,
Much, much better than all the rest.'

'Aye, my friend, we 'ave good beer,
But we don't serve food round 'ere.'
'What? No food! This is bad!
Now you have made me extremely mad!

I've come all this way for a bit of grub
In this very delightful pub.
Now you tell me you don't serve food,
This, my friend, is extremely rude!'

'Sorry mate, but it's the rules,
No serving food and no swimming pools.'
Then the man leapt like a springing gazelle,
The barman's screams were like those from Hell.

At last the man stormed from the pub
And gleefully his hands did rub.
The barman's blood streaked his face,
He laughed at the barman's fall from grace.

George Holmes (13)
Richard Hale School, Hertford

The Shrew

There once was a little bouncing shrew
And a lot about the world this little shrew knew.
He lived in a burrow all warm and cosy,
But although his life was good, he was a bit choosy.

One day this little bouncing shrew
Came across a mouse who said to him, 'Hey you,
Have you got a little food to spare for an animal like me?
'Cause you see, I've just flown right across the sea!'

Said the shrew to the mouse, 'I'm so sorry,
Can't you see that this food is all for me?'
'That's not very nice,' said the mouse to the shrew,
'If you won't let me have it, I'll have to take it from you.'

And just then as they fought near a tree,
They both heard a small hoot from an owl in the tree.
They both froze, right at once,
They had to get out, they had only one chance.

Then the mouse and the shrew both said together,
'We've got to work together.'
And there by that tree the food was divided,
While they were doing so, the owl's hoot subsided.

And from now on (that is forever)
They both only can work together.
They learnt how easily to share,
But they also had friends for whom they would care.

Michael Sledge (12)
Richard Hale School, Hertford

Richard Hale School Vs Sele School

We went to Sele School
To play football,
With no time at all
There was a hand ball.
There was a penalty kick,
The goal made me feel sick.

It was a centre,
They passed it to me,
I controlled it with my knee
And passed it to Fergie.
Fergie played it to Anwar,
He crossed it too far for Ollie,
But luckily it hit the defender on the knee,
It was a corner.

Anwar crossed it to Ollie,
Who hit an excellent volley,
It smashed the back of the net,
Which made the opposition upset.

Freddie Carr (11)
Richard Hale School, Hertford

The Spitfire

The Spitfire is a glorious thing
It has a very strong metal skin
Its defining feature, elliptical wings,
Flying fast, the Rolls Royce engine doing its thing
It won the Battle of Britain
Up and down, flying around
Shooting down enemies that it found
It defended the skies of Britain.

With four machine guns on each wing
It was a beautiful but dangerous thing
Ducking and diving
Shooting and rolling
It won the Battle of Britain
But now it is obsolete
The world moves to a faster beat
But I still find it rather sweet
That it won the Battle of Britain.

Sam Green (13)
Richard Hale School, Hertford

A Tingle In My Fingers

I get a tingle in my fingers
As my hands move down the strings,
I play whatever's in my head
And that can be anything.

A love song or some rock
It doesn't really matter,
I get the same sensation
Like fireworks going off with a clatter!

It's dinner time but I don't care
I want to play some more,
My friends are playing out
But I want to play some more!

Playing the guitar is not a science
Nor is it a sport,
The guitar is a musical language
And an exciting, explorable art.

My dreams are whisked away as I put down the guitar,
The audience are sad
The final act has gone,
But fear not, my friend
And do not weep
As the encores and the music still live on.

Ryan Hyland (11)
Richard Hale School, Hertford

Hamsterz

Hamsters are cool, hamsters are sweet,
Oh how they like to eat and eat.
I have a hamster, she's called Mina,
But my sister likes to call her Davina.
She's really friendly and always wants to play
But sometimes she's mischievous and chews holes
in my jumper,
But I still like my hamster.

Hamsters come in different colours,
Some from Russia, some from China,
But I don't have a favourite,
I like hamsters coz they are cute.
I like the silly things they do,
Like once my hamster ate its p**!

My hamster once won in a competition,
She got a pot of sunflower seeds.
She thought they were yummy,
And then when I took her home, she was very, very chubby.
Oh how I like my hamsters, I think they are very cute,
If you take my hamster, I'll get the gun and shoot.

Christopher Holdys (13)
Richard Hale School, Hertford

Fire

Crackling and burning,
Crumbling and turning,
Orange with red, fiery,
Blue as cold, clearly.
It is fire.

Full of heat,
Hard to beat,
Hot to touch and to obtain,
If you do, you'll be in pain,
Obviously this is fire.

Any colour, it depends,
What you put in it, it always bends,
In flickering colours, red to green,
The tentacles crackle, whipping to a gleam,
This is logically fire.

Full of light,
About to take flight,
Smelling of crisping,
The sound of lisping,
Visibly this is fire.

Its nemesis is water,
Cold and wet,
Whilst fire
Is hot and dire,
Noticeably this is fire.

Fire reminds us of a certain thing,
Whether it be love, pain or pleasures of a king.
Either it be happiness, joy or pleasure
Or sadness, sorrow, high to measure,
Perceptibly, everything is fire.

Thomas Hanner (12)
Richard Hale School, Hertford

The Beginning Of The End

Put on a file, kept in denial,
All is lost in a heartless style,
What once was here has turned to fear,
How do you know what is right
When left is up and loose is tight?

My war is solace dipped in hate,
Given the motives to disintegrate,
We are as one when we crawl on the ground,
This army is Hell's three-headed hound.

To breathe in the dark you taint the light,
Forced to rise together and fall in this fight,
Still we are your children, cutting in the night.

Chaos is unseen when you are not blind,
Order is the evil chained in a line,
While you're looking here they stand right there,
Might they kill you? If not then swear.

We all love to hate when we love each other,
What is this lesson we seldom stand under?
Not enemies, just opposites, chaos and order.

Fear is what is praised these days,
The cold and the dark sets minds ablaze,
As with mindless words and stubborn ways,
Keep the people in an endless daze.

I hope you get the moral of the story,
In writing this I achieve no glory,
Within this poem you will learn a lesson,
One of great sorrow and tragedy.

I just hope that you can see,
As with all our mistakes,
That is our world to be.

Joe Burton (14)
Richard Hale School, Hertford

It's Not Fair

It's really not fair,
Why are they tugging on my underwear?
Why are they making fun of my hair?
I tell the teachers but I know they don't care.

Down the hallways, no hello, just a stare,
I'm not sure if it's the clothes that I wear.
To them I'm just a rat getting clawed by a bear,
Kind of shows the proof cos of the clothes that they tear.

I feel like my destiny is to get doomed,
I just want to sink in the ocean like Neptune.
I go home, all I do is sleep in my bedroom,
Such a small house, I don't get any head or leg room.

Right now I've got a looped rope hanging from the ceiling,
I put my head in the loop, you know the meaning.
The next day I'm on the news in the evening,
With a death letter saying, 'Listen to what people are feeling.'

Leon Lindsay-Ayres (12)
Robert Clack School, Dagenham

Beautiful Lion

Beautiful lion that is so bright,
That silently strides throughout the night,
Always fierce yet ever so proud,
Have you ever heard a roar quite so loud?

It strides bold, graceful and vast,
Has there been such an animal in the past?
Ever so brave and always so grand,
Never to be touched by a human hand.

To be a lion is a dangerous business,
Always fighting to be the right fitness.
Forever risky and forever tough,
Are you sure we have to be so rough?

Oh lovely lion, so brave and so bold,
Stories of Man, they have been told
To avoid such beings at all cost,
Otherwise who knows who'll call the shots?

Kate Graves (11)
Robert Clack School, Dagenham

My Nan! (Lily Knight)

Dear my lovely Grandmother, here is a poem for you.
In this poem I will describe how I love you
From the bottom of my heart,
And because you're so wonderful,
I don't know where to start.
Nan, do you know how much I love you?
Do you know how much I care?
I love to kiss and hug you,
You are like a cuddly bear.
At your house I feel very welcome,
You make it all warm and cosy.
All your children love you,
You're so good to all of us,
So don't go changing now,
I love you the way you are.
Thanks for being you, Nan,
Thanks for filling me with laughter.
I hope you know how much I love you,
So thanks for making me your granddaughter.
One more thing, Nan, thanks for all you've done.

Georgia Louise Davis (11)
Robert Clack School, Dagenham

My Heaven

Heaven brings me such delight
In the shining of its light.
Let the glistening gold pathway
Shine glamorously on my way.

Heaven's light brings such grace
From the maker of its face.
When you look you can see stars, moons
And the sun shining brightly on me.

Shine brightly, shine ghastly,
Shine humorously at me.
Standing in the sun I can see
God, the maker of Heaven and Earth.
Standing in the stars I can see
God, the Father, and standing on the moon
I can see God the Son.
'My loved ones are up there,' I say to myself.

Heaven brings me such delight
I the shining of its light.
Let the glistening gold pathway
Shine glamorously on my way.
Amen.

Grace Nwobi (11)
Robert Clack School, Dagenham

My Mum

Remember when you sang to me
That song you always loved?
The one about the sun shining down on me
And those sweet white turtle doves.

Remember you always tucked me up at night
And made sure I was all right,
Remember when you helped me with my homework
And gave me all those comforting smiles?

You always looked so beautiful
With a lily in your hair,
And those deep blue-coloured eyes you had
That would glisten everywhere.

But now you're not here anymore,
No one to tuck me in bed at night,
To sing me those songs of yours
Or to make sure I feel all right.

No one to help me with my homework,
Or to give me comforting smiles,
And no one to come and help me when I am scared,
Or to make me happy and tell me that they cared.

I always feel so lonely without you,
But there is one thing that I know,
When I see you in my dreams
You tell me you're everywhere I go.

You tell me not to be scared of anything,
And that just because you're not alive,
You're still there for me in my dreams
And in my heart.

Dafina Nishori (12)
Robert Clack School, Dagenham

Once Upon A Time

Once upon a time,
What does it mean?
Other than a fairy tale
With a king and queen.

Once upon a time,
Does that mean a happy ending?
Sometimes there's a bad one,
Or a glamorous wedding.

Once upon a time,
Was it very enchanted?
Princesses, princes,
All your wishes granted.

Once upon a time,
How did that story go?
Of a girl so beautiful,
As pale as snow.

Once upon a time,
Can you see
That every story's magical
And it means a lot to me?

Once upon a time,
Was it a long time ago?
Maybe it was quite recent,
Nobody knows.

Joeann Murphy (12)
Robert Clack School, Dagenham

Heartbroken

Every morning seems the same,
A fake smile and a helpless sigh,
Joins her friends and laughs and plays,
Although all she wants to do is cry.

No one knows what she has to go through
As she covers the bruises with long trousers and sleeves.
Her mum says it's normal but she knows it's not,
No one sees just what she sees.

Her mum tells her to be quiet,
But the teachers always ask,
And she covers the pain
With a painless mask.

She hasn't eaten today,
Her body a lifeless stick,
Her mum comes home, cursing and shouting,
She tries to run, but her mum is too quick.

Her life was cut short
By her aggressive mother,
A lack of confidence
And the pain she used to cover.

Devon Cooney (12)
Robert Clack School, Dagenham

War Did This

Since Daddy left to go to war,
Life hasn't been the same.
One less person at the table,
Just his picture in the frame.

I go outside to play with my friends
But now there's something missing.
I can't call Dad to take me home,
No more hugs and no more kissing.

Who is there to kiss me goodnight?
Who's there to show they care?
Mum doesn't seem to talk anymore,
She whispers, 'It's not fair . . .'

Why did you have to leave Dad?
I thought you loved us all?
You said you would be back soon,
But we're still waiting for the call.

When the planes go overhead,
My life flashes before my eyes.
I've noticed that quite recently
All Mummy does is cries.

Katie Edmead (13)
Robert Clack School, Dagenham

It's Not Fair!

It's not fair,
It's so not fair,
They always take the mickey
Out of my very frizzy hair.

I've had to put up with it
For many, many days,
But very, very soon,
I'll come out of this phase.

It's not fair,
It's so not fair,
But I'll have my revenge,
And for them, it'll be a nightmare!

Victoria Rayment (12)
Robert Clack School, Dagenham

Not Fair!

It's not fair,
She's out there
All because of a stupid dare.

You see my mate,
One I now really hate,
Said she'd give me a date
If I ignored Mrs Tate.

And now
I'm in here
Because of her dare,
Stuff the date,
It's just not fair!

Macawley Evans (11)
Robert Clack School, Dagenham

The Dragon

Dragons are beasts raging with fire,
They are great ambassadors, who eat anything they see,
They are invincible beasts who get much slyer.
Dragons are tall and they have a hot breath,
Anyone who goes near would be like going on a high wire,
People who manage to get near fear death.
Dragons live up in mountains which get higher and higher,
Brave knights who dare to fight will always hold their breath tight,
Although they are strong they should fear dragons' might.
If I were them I would not fight,
Most people who know a dragon
Are already scared and hide away.
A dragon lays in his den and waits,
For someone who is ready to risk his life!

Nikesh Gandhi (13)
Robert Clack School, Dagenham

Friends!

Friends are forever,
They will always stick together.
Without a friend
You're like a ball with no bounce,
An up with no down
And a cherry with no tastes.

Friends are forever,
They will always stick together,
Whatever the weather.

Debora Henriques (11)
Robert Clack School, Dagenham

Rags And Riches

Pick up the remote, switch the TV on,
Change to channel Sky Five-O-One,
Look at Nigeria, heard of India?
Poverty stricken, corruption, invasion,
Draught and dry, no emancipation,
Walk a few miles, life is forever a trial,
For respect in society, shake the hand of indignity,
Hands are dry of currency, falling tears plead for mercy.

We are blinded by greed,
Destination of ambitions, end at money,
So I say, and do heed,
Do not think that this is funny,
Bow your head at those
Who want to wipe your feet?
Keep down your nose,
For humans are they,
And humans are we.

Azaan Akbar (12)
Robert Clack School, Dagenham

The Frog

Ribet, ribet goes the frog,
Ribet, ribet in the fog,
Ribet, ribet all day long,
Oh my, what a song.

Leaping near, leaping far,
No frog likes sticky tar.
Leaping far, leaping near,
Maybe there's a frog that's not afraid to shed a tear.

Bouncing, bouncing everywhere,
Bouncing, bouncing without a care,
Bouncing, bouncing in the road,
Splat!

Ribet, ribet went the frog,
Ribet, ribet in the fog,
Ribet, ribet all day long,
Oh my, what a song.

Rachel Brown (12)
Robert Clack School, Dagenham

I Am Alone

In my head
There is only dread
For the day that lies ahead.

I wonder today
How many people I will drive away
With my own weird little way.

Sometimes I say
Something on the wrong day,
I just wish it would all go away.

Lonely is how I feel,
Even being with friends for a meal,
Lonely is definitely how I feel.

In my head
There is only dread
For the day that lies ahead.

Sometimes I wonder
Why all the thunder?
Maybe it is all just a blunder.

Lonely is how I feel,
Even being with friends for a meal,
Lonely is definitely how I feel.

In my head
There is only dread
For the day that lies ahead.

People say it's just a phase,
But my head feels like a maze,
Just to have to put up with the long days.

Lonely is how I feel,
Even being with friends for a meal,
Lonely is definitely how I feel.

In my head
There is only dread
For the day that lies ahead.

Emma Gadbury (13)
Robert Clack School, Dagenham

Cheetah

Cheetah, you're so fast,
I bet you never come last.
You have such powerful legs,
They pump all day,
So it is easy to catch your prey.

Cheetah, your teeth are so sharp,
Do you like eating carp?
Your jaws go down like a pair of blades,
You have such beautiful spots,
Or are they dots?

Cheetah, you quietly creep towards a deer,
But the deer has no fear.
Run, run, run goes the chase
Until *snap!*
His prey is on the cheetah's lap.

Cheetah, you take dinner to your cubs,
All the cubs love their grub.
Cheetah, sit down and rest,
The cubs bite into the meat
Safely, right near Mum's feet.

Cheetah, with your eyes so bright,
Helps you see well at night,
Searching for danger, left and right,
Along comes a lion
With teeth of iron.

Cheetah, *roar!*
The lion runs away so now, Cheetah,
You can lay down and snore.
Morning has come,
Cheetah and the cubs play happily,
Until next time . . .

Adam Pamplin (12)
Robert Clack School, Dagenham

Love

What is love?
I pray to the heavens above.
Do we need it?
Maybe just a bit.
I need love,
Do you?

Love can be expressed in many different ways,
I've thought of that over the recent days.
I hit and bang those dusty trays
Which lay in the cold, dark corner,
To think of a way that I can express the love I possess.
My friend, Ted, said love is an emotion,
I thought of that while I used the liquidised lotion.
Can love be in the form of a potion?

Love, what a feeling,
How do people contain it?
One minute up,
One minute down.
Is love controllable?
Can you control this strange emotion?
I definitely can't.
I wonder, can anybody?

Toluwa Dada (12)
Robert Clack School, Dagenham

Unbelievable Dog

Dog, dog,
In the night,
Disturbing the animals at moonlight,
Never again would they have a fright,
Because the dog is asleep.

In the morning the dog will lay,
Rolling about in the hay.
Then the farmer will come and say,
'Get off my hay or you'll have to pay!'

After hearing what the farmer had to say,
The dog jumped up and went off to play.
Maybe the dog will listen some day,
Because I don't want him laying in my hay!

Towards the evening he would settle down,
Hoping that he wouldn't get up and frown,
But when the time reaches six o'clock,
He would run upstairs and get my frock.

At midnight he would sit on my lap,
Playing around with my baseball cap,
But then I think of my dead cat
And hope my dog will live longer than that!

Tamika Arnold (12)
Robert Clack School, Dagenham

It's Not Fair

It's not fair we're judged by the colour of our skin,
Black, brown or white,
This is the same world we live in,
Everyone is equal, everyone is bright.

Tall, short, fat or thin,
Bad, nice, annoying or smart,
Being a different colour shouldn't be a sin,
The world is a big piece of art.

They sit in the bath rubbing at their skin
Trying to turn it white, but then it bleeds.
What type of world do we live in?
Is this what our world needs?

If someone calls you ugly, they're ugly too.
They don't know what they're saying.
Everyone is equal and that is true,
Just call to God and keep praying.

It's not fair we're judged by the colour of our skin,
Black, brown or white.
This is the same world we live in,
Everyone is equal, everyone is bright.

Navdeep Snotra (12)
Robert Clack School, Dagenham

Questions

Bullies think they are big and hard . . . are they?
Bullies think they are strong when they pick on people . . .
Are they?
Why are there bullies in this world?
Do you think the world would be a better place without bullies?
Do you think bullies could stand up to someone their own size
Or is it because they can't sand up to the big ones
That they have to pick on the small ones?
Is it because bullies have got a hard life
And they don't know how to handle it?
Do you think bullies are nice people to be with?
Do you think that bullies are hard because they smoke?
Do you think they are hard because
They try to get people to take drugs?
Why can't bullies respect other people?
Why can't bullies just be nice people?
Why should people put up with bullies?
Why should bullies make people
Get involved with drugs and fags?
Why does there have to be violence all the time?
Why can't bullies do something else
Instead of making other people feel small?
Do bullies think it is fun to pick on people?
Is it because they don't get what they want in life?
Why can't they go somewhere like a boxing club
To lose their temper?
Why do bullies like picking on people?
Why are there bullies in this world?
Have you got any answers for me?

Jade Reader (13)
St Nicholas' School, Southend-on-Sea

Palace

The rising damp creeping up,
crumbling, fumbling up
walls like watery
spiders,
flies on clock faces, chimes
in the empty shell, like
cockles or lobster.

Cards of glass in clumsy
chandelier-fingers, frozen
notes floating in idol hands
of gold and silence.

Knuckles wrapped in oak and
solitude, smell of disinfectant
dripping like perfume.

In musty bottles thick
with gasping memories, choked
revelation under leather
gloves and autumn trees,
echoes of screams, taunted,
tied to sideboards with coins
and ladders, naked crawls
like trains on parkwalk tracks,
grinding wheels and pistons like
skeletal arms.

Across the lake, rowboat
drifting, they lie, washed
up, swept by uncertain tides
of time, space and taxes, free
from the fuhrer handshake
stranglehold, left on the
valley's relief with
grassy backs and consciences.

Circling descents over crimson
and sandstone.

He sat in his balsa
desert, tea-heavy and
paperweight shy. A
caffeine headphone oasis.

Tom Macarte (17)
Sharnbrook School & Community College, Sharnbrook

'Bout My Generation

A very confused little girl,
Her smile as white as a pearl,
Her room packed with fluffy bears,
Who might touch them, who will dare?
Her favourite foods are burgers and chips,
She can still taste it lingering on her lips.
Her favourite drink Coca-Cola,
Her favourite animal . . . can you guess?
Yes, a polar.

Cherise Mask (11)
Springwood High School, King's Lynn

What Am I?

I'm as curious as a cat . . .
I'm as dumb as a dog . . .
I'm as devious as a donkey . . .
I'm as mad as a cow . . .
I'm as sweet as a butterfly . . .
I'm as quiet as a mouse . . .
I'm as calm as a camel . . .
Am I really all that?

Katie Daines (11)
Springwood High School, King's Lynn

When I Was Small/When I Was Old

When I Was Small

I had big brown eyes, flowing blonde curls,
My favourite pastime mowing the lawn
With my grandad's big mower.
Mum called me dude and I was never rude.
The favourite pastime of Nan and I was walking the dog
And feeding the foxes at the end of the lane.

When I Was Old

Mum still calls me dude but I can be quite rude.
Football is my passion
And wearing the right gear, my fashion.
My hair is ginger-brown,
My face is covered in freckles,
And my great big smile.

Cameron Jones (12)
Springwood High School, King's Lynn

Always Believe

(In loving memory of Lee Colangelo)

Even though you are gone,
I know you are always there for me.
I didn't know you for long,
But your spirit will go on forever.

Although life can be rough
And I can't go on,
I'll think of you
And remember how much you loved me.

I know I will miss you
And people around me will try to help,
But I know you are safe
And you will look down on me from Heaven
And be proud.

Katharine Colangelo (13)
Springwood High School, King's Lynn

Talkin' 'Bout My Generation

When I was small I was sweet . . .
Maybe not, so you're in for a treat!
I loved to get muddy by jumping in puddles,
I'd get my hands stuck together,
Which left me in muddles!
Last of all I loved to swim,
My mum loathes it so let's get her in!

Zoe Kirby (11)
Springwood High School, King's Lynn

Looking Through The Eyes Of . . .

Looking through the eyes of a child,
Looking at the pale and wrinkled face
Of her dying grandfather,
Wondering why it is him in hospital,
Wondering how he is suffering
And whether it is a bad disease.

Looking through the eyes of a child
Being bullied,
No one liking him or her,
Wondering what they got out of it
And whether they care,
Wondering what other nasty plans
They have for him or her.

Looking through the eyes of a child
Suffering bad pain,
With their parents sitting there
Wondering if they are going to live or die,
Wondering how they feel
And how they are going to feel
If anything happens.

Maria Pike (13)
Stalham High School, Norwich

If Only They Knew

It doesn't matter, they say.
They don't have to suffer the day.
If only they knew.

The sneering looks,
We pretend not to care,
Each day is a battle.
If only they knew.

The day ends.
Hearts sing with silent joy.
'How was your day?'
'Fine.'
If only they knew.

India Cottiss (15)
Stalham High School, Norwich

Please Cut Along The Dotted Lines

Please cut along the dotted lines,
You can start at the wrists, I don't mind.
The blackened nails, the blackened hair,
Just a sign that I don't care.
I've done it before, that you know,
Because the scars on my wrists clearly show.
The ones across are the lack of attention,
The ones that are straight, well those I don't mention.
Just because of our colourless clothes
Make us the people that everyone loathes,
But I've seen that boy with so many friends,
Following the fashions and latest trends.
The cool, kind, popular type,
The one that all the girls obviously like.
And just because I'm always excluded,
Just this once I want to be included . . .

Samantha Chadwick (14)
Stalham High School, Norwich

A Whistle In The Wind

All I hear is a whistle in the wind
On a lovely hot summer's day.

All I hear is a whistle in the wind
When I go out to play.

All I hear is a whistle in the wind
Every single day.

Gemma Wilding (12)
Stalham High School, Norwich

War

She reminisces
They had almost got her as well
She escaped, they swore at her
They called her names she never knew
Can't run a country
The world rippled in her mind
What did they mean?
She was a child, her country was her town
And her town was just fine
Their comments were out of line
Her town was family, they shared their love
Yet the people in green disagreed
They said more than that
They said that they were dangerous
They shoot and murder
Yet the blame was on her
What danger?
They said they had no respect
Respect is earned, fear is instilled.

Batool Wali (13)
Stopsley High School, Luton

My Magic Box

(Based on 'Magic Box' by Kit Wright)

I will put in the box . . .
A piece of cheesy pizza,
The cheesiness of the pizza
All in my mouth.

I will put in the box . . .
A lion with a rumbling,
A sip of the dirty water from the lake,
A leaping spark of an electric fish.

I will put in the box . . .
Two comments spoken by a French person,
The last joke from an uncle,
The last kiss from an auntie
And the first laugh from a baby sister.

I will put in the box . . .
A ninth season and a blue moon,
A monkey with glasses
And a person with a tail.

My box is made of pancakes
But you can't see inside,
With pictures of elephants all over the lid.
The hinges are like frogs' feet.

I shall swim to my box
On the Atlantic sea leading to my box,
The colour of the sun as it sets,
The bright red setting on the sea.

Ryan Parsons (12)
Stopsley High School, Luton

When LV Had A Supply!

LV was a naughty class,
Their teacher was in despair,
And one day she was too ill to teach,
She'd eaten a dodgy pear.

So that day LV had a supply,
Mr Gullible was his name,
When LV heard his name they thought,
Now this is going to be a fun game!

'Hello children,' he said brightly,
As LV smiled sweetly.
'Good morning Sir,' they said,
As they did their ties a little too neatly.

'Sir,' said Alex Muton,
The naughtiest of them all,
'Miss always has a glass of water from the fish tank
Before the register call.'

After registration and Sir's refreshing drink,
It was maths and Becky ran out of the class.
'Where is she going?' asked Sir.
Harriet then answered, 'She's a Spacearian,
she's celebrating the birthday of Mars.'

By the end of the day, LV were amazed
That Mr Gullible still hadn't caught on to their games.
And all the way home they were laughing and cheering
Because they knew Mr Gullible knew none of their names.

Lizzy Fretwell (12)
Stopsley High School, Luton

The Magic Box

(Based on 'Magic Box' by Kit Wright)

I will put in the box . . .
An Indian princess dancing around the sunset,
Paint being flicked in France,
A cool breeze cackling among the stars,
Hawaiian pineapples falling off trees.

I will put in the box . . .
An electrifying volcano spilling out with lava,
The tropical sensation from the Hawaiian breeze,
The tip of an iceberg from the Antarctic.

I will put in the box . . .
A voodoo doll pierced with pins,
A baby's smile like the sun going down,
The glowing gaze from a long-lost relative.

I will put in the box . . .
A surfing horse in the deep blue sea,
A thirteenth month on every year,
A bunny living in a swimming pool.

My box will be fashioned with the
Glitter from the Queen's crown,
With alligator skin roughed around the edge.
The opening of the box will be nicely
Decorated with tiles all around the edge.

I shall swim in my box
Upon the glistening sea of the Indian ocean,
Then bungee jump upon the
Shimmering stars shining like the sun.

Lauren Squires (13)
Stopsley High School, Luton

War

The cobbled stone streets,
The burning heat,
Humans paraded
Like vile beasts.

Every heartbreaking step,
Every heavy drawn breath,
Living in famine and poverty,
So close to the gates of death.

Their feet dragged across the ground,
Walking for many heartless miles
To the arrival of certain death,
Punished without fair trials.

Every breath forced against their will,
They were dragged out of their homes.
Lives spent in intense famine,
Until they rot to the bone.

A life spent suffering unjustly,
Just because of their identity.
Without blue eyes and blond hair,
Dreaming of a world with peace and serenity.

Hidden away in extreme terror,
Afraid of every voice,
Not being able to breathe
For fear of losing a choice.

War is as black as death,
A smoke-filled heart of pain.
The world is turning corrupt
For one man's need for fame.

Abigail Hettle (13)
Stopsley High School, Luton

My Family

I have a great family,
Who are always smiley,
They're always in my heart
And they are all really smart.

My sister is really cute
And she really loves to play the flute.
Sometimes she can get over the top
So I tell her to stop.

I have a very funny dad,
But sometimes he can be sad.
He used to be in the army
And he loves to eat salami.

I have a very smart mum,
She really loves to chew chewing gum.
My mum appreciates her job
And her favourite food is corn on the cob.

Vato Beridze (13)
Stopsley High School, Luton

Riddle

I walk behind you always,
Slowly and stealthily.
Some people fear me,
While others remember me in joy.
I unravel many secrets
That have been long forgotten.
You all have me
From the day you are born.
With my two siblings
I rule over time.
What am I?

A: The past.

Tina Mistry (13)
Stopsley High School, Luton

The Magic Box

(Based on 'Magic Box' by Kit Wright)

I will put in the box . . .
The sweet aroma of Italian food,
The heat of the oven door as it opens,
And the swirling string of spaghetti.

I will put in the box . . .
The clear blue water of the Australian beach,
The beautiful tropical fish
And the yellow, golden sand.

I will put in the box . . .
The biggest cake in the world,
The swirling chocolate
And the whipped cream of the tastiest cake.

I shall put some snow on the top of Mount Everest,
The ice from Antarctica.

Gary Sheridan (13)
Stopsley High School, Luton

Nonsense Poem

The lion is a weak fish,
He uses his tail as a guide to swim,
He is a vegetarian that loves to eat steak,
And has a fin attached to his limb.

The lion has blunt teeth,
He hates to hunt and sleeps at home,
He is too scared to fight
And sorts out his mane with a comb.

The lion lives in the Arctic,
He has no fur and isn't cold,
He is all alone
And has no mane, making him bald.

Dilbir Kundi (13)
Stopsley High School, Luton

Shadows Of Love

I walk through the moonlit shadows
Onto the pale sand,
All the memories come flooding back,
Walking with you hand in hand.

I stare out towards the rippling sea,
The waves lapped endlessly on the shore,
Stars shimmered sadly overhead,
Cherishing those memories from before.

My silver hair flowing behind my back,
My turquoise eyes as clear as glass,
The breeze flowing noiselessly.
How could I let time pass?

The shells gleamed magically,
Scattered around the beach,
I see a vision of you,
I stretch out my hand to reach.

A sudden wave crashes down,
Your image is shattered . . .
Shattered into a million pieces,
Just like our love . . .

Tanzila Hakeem (13)
Stopsley High School, Luton

Mad For Food!

There was a person that liked to eat,
Clenched his hands and stamped his feet.

Then they said, 'What's up dude?'
'I really am in the mood for food!'

Then he ate this and that,
Ate too much and became fat.

He became mad and killed a goose,
Cut out its brain and made some juice.

Killed so much he became crazy,
Someone that was very lazy.

Couldn't move and ate just bread,
Ate too little and dropped down dead.

Martin Tang (12)
Stopsley High School, Luton

The Basketball

The clock is running down,
The game is on the line,
Ten seconds till the buzzer,
There ain't much time.
We're behind by a point,
But our team's got the ball,
All eyes are on the coach
To make the game-winning call.

Josh England (15)
Stopsley High School, Luton

My Holiday Poem

Children playing in the pool
Sitting in the sun
Parents getting a suntan
And eat hot cross buns.

Families having dinner at a restaurant
Walking to the beach, playing in the sea
Smelling the fresh air
And getting chased by a bee.

Playing games with family
Looking at the view of the blue sea
Having an ice-cold drink
And telling a wasp to flee.

Going to a place which is sunny
Or going to a place which is cold
Getting sunburnt all the time
Also people being bold.

Birds flying by
Reading a book in the sun
Looking at the nice orange and yellow sand
And children having fun.

Molly Campion (12)
Stopsley High School, Luton

New Year's Eve

The party has started
Friends and family are coming round
The food looks delicious
And the music is blaring in the background

Only a few minutes to go
Until the clock strikes midnight
And the fireworks get let off
They go up at such a height

Dad has set up the fireworks
They will soon be up in the sky
Mum is fussing over the food
It looks like she's about to cry

Not long now, the countdown begins
10, 9, 8, 7, 6 it says
5, 4, 3, 2, 1, *Happy New Year*
And everyone goes off to their partying ways

The fireworks are so bright
With yellow, pinks and greens
They go up and fade into the sky
It's like they were never seen

The party is over now
And we've turned out all the lights
I am really tired now
Goodnight.

Kimberley Beardwell (12)
Stopsley High School, Luton

My Magic Box

(Based on 'Magic Box' by Kit Wright)

I will put in the box . . .
An American super-size burger with fries,
The hustle and bustle of Delhi,
The passion of Italian life.

I will put in the box . . .
The furious flames of fire,
A leaf from an ancient tree,
The purest water on Earth.

I will put in the box . . .
The last laugh of a dying man,
The tallest man on Earth,
A Polish man singing.

I will put in the box . . .
A fat man on a bike,
A dictionary with nothing inside,
A penguin having a warm bath.

My box will be fashioned with
Glue and grass that smells of chocolate,
Hinges made of bricks.

I will sail in the box
On a speedboat along the shimmering sea
To an island and end on a perfect beach.
I will lie and watch the sunset while drinking beer.

Jordan Newbery (13)
Stopsley High School, Luton

The Magic Box

(Based on 'Magic Box' by Kit Wright)

I will put in the box . . .
The rich, exotic smells that fill the air,
The sounds from the chaotic coliseum,
The warm sunset over the calm sea.

I will put in the box . . .
The whistling wind and the first crash of lightning on
a stormy sea,
A drop of water from the Atlantic Ocean,
An icicle from the cold North Pole.

I will put in the box . . .
A roar from the biggest lion in the jungle,
A piece of fur from the tallest giraffe,
A puppy playing in the garden.

I will put in the box . . .
An eighth day and a flying ostrich,
A drop of dry rain and a cold sun,
And the fastest tortoise.

My box will be fashioned from gold and silver,
With scales on the lid and windows on the sides.
Its hinges will be the most expensive silk.

I shall go diving in my box
In the Great Barrier Reef,
Then go to see all the twinkling lights
Of the eventful New York City.

Shelby Baker (12)
Stopsley High School, Luton

My Magic Box

(Based on 'Magic Box' by Kit Wright)

In my box you will find . . .
The golden grains of Spain's sand,
The healing power of Bulgaria's salty sea
The frosty touch of Sweden's bitter cold snow.

In my box you will find . . .
A plucked thorn of a radiant red rose,
A drip of poison from a snake's snarl,
The sweet scent of Norfolk's lavender gardens.

In my box you will find . . .
The excitement of a child on Christmas Eve,
The patter of feet from a baby's first steps,
The wishes of people on the waterfall's floor.

In my box you will find . . .
A twenty-fifth hour and an eight-day week,
The first and last ray of the sunlight,
A tear cried from underwater.

My box is padded with rainbow petals;
Its lid is melted birthstones.
The outside is driftwood washed up on the world's beaches,
Its cracks filled with best friends' secrets!

I shall sail in my box on the frosty top of Mount Everest
And then drift upon a lost tropical island
Isolated from the rest of the world.

Abigail Irons (12)
Stopsley High School, Luton

Dead Inside

I feel like I don't belong here
Don't fit into this world
A world where no one understands
Where everyone is disposable

I have no real purpose
No goals to achieve
No dreams to fulfil
No one to care about

In a society where dominance is the key
Everyone brainwashed into one belief
One dominating thought
The idea that power is immortalising

With this thought people try and rule
Places that aren't there to be ruled
Civilisations that should be left alone
Humans that need to understand

To understand that power comes at a price
A price that none are willing to pay
But at some point all have to
The ultimate sacrifice

I am alone in this world
This is because I already understand
I've already paid the price
I understand the power within

The price was greater than I thought
But I accepted my curse
Every day it burns away at me
Taking from me my very soul

I am dead inside
Never to be reborn.

Aidan Broom (15)
Stopsley High School, Luton

The Lucky Pen

I have a lucky pen,
It is silver and gold,
I carry it around with me,
It is very old.

It hasn't lost its colour,
It still looks brand new,
It's been handed down to me
From my aunty Blue.

Today it started sparkling,
Very, very bright,
Yellow, gold and silver,
Shining in the light.

It never meant to do that,
Sparkle in the light,
But then something happened,
The pen flew out of sight.

I'm sure it will come back to me,
It is my lucky pen,
But maybe it won't come back to me,
And go to cousin Ben.

Lucinda Stallard (12)
The Heathcote School, Stevenage

Invisible

If I was invisible for a day,
I know exactly what I would do.
I would spy on all the teachers,
Creep up on them and say *boo!*

I'd eat the chocolate cake
And no one would know it was me.
I'm normally only allowed one slice,
Now I can have three!

But now I miss being me,
It's not nice being unseen.
I miss being with my friends,
Being invisible is mean.

I'm glad it's the end of the day,
I can stop being invisible now.
I look in a mirror, I am back,
I know it's me, but how!

I'm back and I'm glad,
I don't like invisibility.
It's really not that good,
I'm just glad to be me!

Rebecca Tremlett (11)
The Heathcote School, Stevenage

Control

He controlled everything,
The money,
My work,
My life.
I didn't know what to do.
If I wanted to go out,
He would come with me.
If I wanted to go out with friends
I had to have his approval.
If I had to do some shopping,
He would go instead of me.

Now he is gone,
I am free,
I won't get hurt
Anymore.

Thank you.

Luke Cox (13)
The Heathcote School, Stevenage

Death

He pulled the trigger, *bang*.
He killed the man, *crash*.
He fell to the floor, *thud*.
He killed a man . . . silence.

He took his keys, cards and wallet,
He took his life with just one bullet.

M anslaughter?
U gly.
R easonable?
D eath.
E very day?
R IP.

Stabbed, shot, strangled,
Smothered, overdose,
Suicide, hanged, death!

Jessica Roberts (12)
The Heathcote School, Stevenage

The Door

There was a knock at the door,
I ran and tripped,
I slid across the floor,
I was lying out cold.

Lying in the hospital bed,
Everyone standing there beside me,
Where I smashed and fractured my head,
I could die right there and then.

That night I had a dream
Of a man dressed in white
And it may seem
He was trying to take my life that night.

Two months later, still in bed.
Why me, me Master Fred?
And now I am dead,
All because I broke my head,

All because of the knock at the door!

Corey Todd (12)
The Heathcote School, Stevenage

Drugs To Homeless

It was 1998,
I got this stuff from my mate.

He said it made you glad,
After a while it made me sad.

I took some more,
I was near death's door.

But I was not dead,
Doctor said to stay in bed.

I got introduced to this new stuff,
Didn't make me rough.

I spent too much,
I took too much.

Now I sit on the street,
No shoes on my feet.

I got no more of it,
I must be an addict.

I spent my house and car for it,
I'm definitely a drug addict.

Matthew Temple (12)
The Heathcote School, Stevenage

Teenagers

Everybody thinks I'm bad
I'm just a 13-year-old lad
Being followed in the shops
Even stalked by the cops
Is it because I wear a hood?
Stay indoors? Yes I should.
I am already under control
The police have missed a giant hole
My mate is running down the street
His heart must have skipped a beat
He couldn't keep his hands at bay
He struggled for the whole day
I'm standing in the road, gobsmacked
In the police car he goes packed.
I suppose I have to go to court
Because of something he hadn't bought
But not all teenagers are like that
He was just acting like a prat
If you look I'm sure you'll find
A teenager that's very kind
With no weight on his shoulders
My mate must have been carrying boulders
His sentence was three years in jail
Soon he'll be released on bail
But I go on with my life
Knowing I've got no strife
Not all teenagers are bad!

Darren Gormley (13)
The Heathcote School, Stevenage

The Ghost Of Mr Pebbles

It's not that easy working in a circus,
So it might seem on the surface.
I was here for three years,
The balancing cat, they used to call me.
Such haunting memories in my head,
But still we rarely got fed.
My most dreaded one is about my cousins,
Well more than that actually, they were dozens.
They gathered them in nets,
Ascending them higher
From a special bundle
Onto a bonfire.
The crowd's reaction sickened me,
I could hear shrieks of laughter
As the cats howled for their happy ever after.
They screeched with pain as their skins were roasted
And their bodies finally carbonised like toast.
After that the crowd took the ashes home,
Believing it brought good luck,
But they realised at the end of the day
That they had just tortured our lives away.
By now you're probably wondering how I died,
Well this is where the story begins.
The cage guard had my mouth, nose and eyes glued shut,
But that wasn't all, he had my ears cut.
Gentle as can be, he led me to the cellar,
Kicked me down the stairs.
I was left there to die,
Rotting away for six whole days,
But not a single tear from my eye.

Kapaya Chimpampwe (12)
The Heathcote School, Stevenage

Tragedy

I'm sitting in the church
With my head in my hands,
I can't believe it's happened,
My best friend gone forever.

We were sitting on the bus
To go to the field trip.
We were sitting at the back with all our friends,
But we two moved because it was crowded.

Everyone laughing, playing around,
All of a sudden the bus screeched.
It rolled eight times,
Landed with a thud.

I was trying to move but I was stuck.
I heard the sirens down the hill.
People stopped and stared.
Now I couldn't find my friend.

I shouted her name, but no reply.
The people calmed me down.
I was safe and sound in the ambulance,
But my friend was nowhere to be seen.

Then they told me she was dead.
I fell back and cried a silent tear,
Saw her parents crying too.

I'm in church saying a prayer
For my true friend who died.
That's life. Life is not fair!

Laura Norgan (13)
The Heathcote School, Stevenage

Help Me!

I am running through the streets,
My bag hanging off my arm.
I can hear Dad calling me,
But far away, he can do no harm.

I call but no one hears me,
I am here all alone.
I fall but no one sees me,
I am far away from home.

I turn around but I can't see, tears are in my eyes,
Thank God he now can't reach me,
I am happy - there is no disguise.

I remember as I left the house,
Mum on the floor screaming, 'Run!'
Blood was running down her face
Because of what he had done.

Her eyes were full of fear,
Dad's hands above his head,
And then he turned and stared at me
With a look that would scare the dead.

He struck me hard on the face as I reached for the door,
I opened it and started running,
Now here I am, on the floor.

Then a light shone across my face,
Someone had come out of a house,
They reached down to offer me a kind, warm hand,
I took it as quietly as a mouse.

Now I am in a new family
A kind and loving one,
And now I can try and forget
The harm that was once done.

Francesca Allard (12)
The Heathcote School, Stevenage

I Am A Football

I am a football
Sitting in a field,
Right now I am alone
But see players running down the hill.

I hope our team wins
And gets the golden shield.
It would be nice to see them happy,
After all, they clean their babies' nappies.

Oh my God we've scored a goal,
Oh no, be careful! I just saw a mole.
Oh good gracious me, you're
Running to the pole,
Do be careful . . .

Oooh, that must have hurt,
Great, there's blood on your shirt.
I don't want to go near you,
Then I'd want to go splat.

That was great, we won the shield,
I've had a great time on the field.

But now we have to celebrate,
So goodbye for now.
Hope we meet again,
But not just now.

Laura Whitaker (11)
The Heathcote School, Stevenage

My World

If the world could be changed, my way would be the best.
Let's see, here I go again!

At school the bullies and baddies would
Have to be chucked away
And fun and games every day!
Out in the playground very far
I would be crowded like a superstar!
Here I go again!

At home a big house awaits me
I have my own key
Just especially for me!
Here I go again!

My family, we are happy as can be,
My dog, my grandparents and me!
It is like someone has cast a spell!
Here I go again!

Let's see, what is left?
Oh yes, I have to be changed too!
I think I should be brand new!
Sugar and spice and all things nice!
My world could be just right
Peace and quiet night and day!
But my world is only a dream
And a dream that should come true
Let's keep it a secret, me and you!

Grace Howard (13)
The Heathcote School, Stevenage

Home All Alone

I'm lost and alone,
There's no one at home.

I'm sad and hungry
And surrounded in fungi.

I can feel myself wasting away,
I'm sure I'll be gone by the end of the day.

No one around to help me so
And how was I supposed to know

They'd take me home and leave me there
Like they didn't care

I'm just a puppy,
Small and mucky.

They took me in and gave me milk
And a blanket made of silk.

Hannah Rayner (13)
The Heathcote School, Stevenage

Frightened

I am the thing all alone
Hidden in the shadows
Not wanting to be shown

I am the thing that most people dread
Nobody can see me
You imagine me in your head

I can make you in the darkness all alone
It is mostly silent
Apart from a moan

I can haunt you for the rest of your life
You can see yourself dead
Because of the knife

I am the thing that you will always see
And it won't be you
It will be me.

Alexander Mills (13)
The Heathcote School, Stevenage

What Will The Future Hold?

What will the future hold?
The serious question everyone dreads . . .

Why does the ozone layer have holes in?
Will the sea level rise?
How will we react in the future?

What will the future hold?
The serious question everyone dreads . . .

Will the future generation care
Or just reply 'It's not our problem'?
Can we help the future?
Will we have to change our lifestyle dramatically?

What will the future hold?
The serious question everyone dreads . . .

In the year 3000 will we live underwater?
Will population decrease?
Will animals die on our behalf?

The only solution is to do our bit . . .

Willeke Roden (13)
The Princess Helena College, Preston

No One Knows Who I Am

I try to act kind and I try to be nice
Thinking about having to be thinking twice.
They're all sure that they know me,
As if we've known each other an eternity,
But I can hear their voices behind my back,
Only the truth is what they lack.
Their voices ringing inside my head,
I'm not in a fight but I feel so dead.
Sometimes life feels like a great big scam;
No one knows who I am.

Sophie Walton (12)
The Princess Helena College, Preston

Sounds So Simple

'I want to change the world.'
Sounds so simple.
My first target is to tell all the lazy losers that litter
To leave the lanes alone.
The next move is to make
All the children of mischief
Go out and play all day,
Not sit and slouch.
Then I'll give those teens a talking to
And tell them not to text.
But how do I please everyone?
'I want to change the world.'
Sounds so simple.

Megan Williams (13)
The Princess Helena College, Preston

The Real Me

On this side of the door is what you think you see,
A young 12-year-old girl
Who's just moved schools,
Looking shy and nervous.

But on the other side of the door
Is the real me,
A mature, bold and confident person,
Who cares for others and not just herself.

I know that I will grow up and probably change,
But the door I decide to be behind
Will not stop the real me!

Annabella Terry (12)
The Princess Helena College, Preston

My Life Is What I Make Of It

I am a typical 13-year-old girl
My life is one long busy whirl
I go to school, I ride my horse
My mum books me a sailing course

Sometimes I think the world's gone crazy
Children are rude, unkind and lazy
No one wants to go to school
They just want to break every rule.

It's hard to see where my life will go
I struggle to learn and long to know
Where I will be in twenty years' time
I hope I am happy and my life is sublime

I am more than what you see
I think a lot more what I want to be
I am lucky to have a good life
I hope I'll make a good mother and wife.

Isabel Wright (13)
The Princess Helena College, Preston

The Drunken Mother

I lie in bed, watching a star,
My mum is drinking in the bar.
She drinks all day and drinks all night,
When will she realise it's just not right?

She staggers home each morning,
I have just woken up and I'm still yawning.
It pains me to see her this way,
Wasting her life, day by day.

No matter where I go, I smell it.
She won't stop, not even for a bit.
She pours a glass of Chardonnay,
And this is the end of another day.

Victoria Paxman (12)
The Princess Helena College, Preston

Examinations

As the noisy children bundle in from the playground,
The papers are being laid out in the cold, echoing exam hall,
Ready and waiting for the pupil to sit in front of them.
As Sally wanders into the hall, her heart is in her mouth,
All of this revision just for this.
She knows inside her that she must not fail.
As she pulls out a chair to sit on,
It drags along the floor in a cold, reverberating way.
She sits down.
The loud bell rings through the room to signal the start.
There is a sound of rustling papers and pens
frantically scribbling
And Sally starts to write but cannot control her shaking hand.
She thinks, *is this what life is about?*
Is it?
Is it?

Hannah Clarke (12)
The Princess Helena College, Preston

My Life

I am the girl with flaming spirit,
I am the girl with amazing lyrics,
I am the girl who will fight the bully,
I am the girl who won't be silly,
I am the girl who takes it serious,
Work makes me live, doesn't make me delirious.
Think of me as born to live,
My brain's a thinker, not a sieve.
I work till I'm done,
Not just for a job or just for fun.
Do what you're told,
Be brave, not bold,
This is a life,
The life of me.

Ali Sadler (12)
The Princess Helena College, Preston

I Want To Be Me!

People say you should be more like . . .
More clever and more sporty.
All I want is to be me!

I want to have fun,
Enjoy my life,
Live my life my way,
Not how people tell me, except for teachers!
All I want is to be me!

Exams, exams, exams,
Yes I know I have exams,
I know I have to revise
But I don't need you to pressurise me!
All I want is to be me!

There's a new style everyone has,
A new pair of trousers,
New stationery everyone has,
All I want is to be me!

Katie Ellis (12)
The Princess Helena College, Preston

The Spirit Of The Night

There is a spirit all along
Who cannot rest,
She has a duty to fulfil.

Before she was a spirit there was a man,
A man who took away her laughter,
A man who took away her love.

This man gave many jobs to the undertakers
And left the spirit with nothing,
The spirit had no one.

The spirit tried to run and hide,
But there was no way out from the horrible man.
He got her at the mid of night.

The spirit wants to get him back.
For all he has done to her in her life,
She wanted to get him back . . .

And I did!

Sophia Kelly (13)
The Princess Helena College, Preston

Will It Last?

I started a new school
But not just any school,
It was high school.
I was the new girl, nobody knew me,
Will it last?

I'm in Year 8 now,
I have a great time with all my friends,
Sleepovers, parties and all the rest,
Will it last?

I am scared about the future,
Choosing GCSEs, doing GCSEs,
Choosing my A levels, doing my A levels,
I feel as if I will never be ready,
Will it last?

I am looking forward to growing up,
Learning to drive and becoming smarter,
But I don't want to leave school and have to say goodbye,
My sadness and happiness,
It will last.

Eleanor Pearce (13)
The Princess Helena College, Preston

How Did This Happen?

(In loving memory of my dear nan)

People do not realise how so much can change in one night,
How you can go to bed feeling fine
And then wake up and everything is gone.

There is nothing more to my life now
Than just lying on this bed,
All I can do is think,
Remember how my life used to be,
Trying to summarise how I got here.

I always used to say that life's too short to waste it,
And now lying here, I believe I was correct.
Knowing I will never walk again,
It seems like the world has given up on me,
Like nobody cares.

So who am I now?
I am the person in the bed on the left hand side.
There are so many questions that I need answers for.
Why won't they tell me what I want to know?
What the main one comes down to is . . .
How did this happen?

Sophie Bird (13)
The Princess Helena College, Preston

Can You Guess?

They comfort you when you are down,
Sometimes they act like total clowns.

Some you remember forever and ever,
Some are daft and some are clever.

You chat and gossip when you are out,
You talk in confidence without a doubt.

Every day they are there for you,
In all things that you say and do.

Do you know the subject here?
If you don't then have no fear,
For it is friends,
Which some of you have guessed.
Believe me now, they really are the best . . .

. . . things about this generation.

Laura Purvis (13)
The Princess Helena College, Preston

What Will The People Of The Future Think?

Will they think I'm old and frail?
Will they think I'm useless and cold?
What will they think? Nobody knows.

Will they say computers are old?
Will they say cars are slow?
What will they say? Nobody knows.

Will they talk a different language?
Will they have what we have only dreamed of?
What will they do? Nobody knows.

Will they find there is life on Mars?
Will they find the blame for global warming?
What will they find? Nobody knows.

Will we be eliminated from the face of the Earth?
Will everyone live to be at least 100?
What will happen? I don't know.

Olivia Rigby (12)
The Princess Helena College, Preston

War

I wake up not knowing what to expect.
There are people out there waiting and asking for help,
But then some are just there to make my life a misery.

So here I am, sitting in a tank,
The blazing hot sun burning down on me,
Cream and brown army kit everywhere.

I will admit I'm scared,
Not just for me but for all those lives around me.
I am scared,
Who knows how long I will live,
Who knows what all these people are thinking?
Seeing all these strangers,
Me,
Coming and changing their lives!

I want to help.
Boom!
That's my cue,
I'm off again.

Heart racing,
Palms sweating,
Wish me luck,
Who knows what's going to happen?

Hannah Routledge (13)
The Princess Helena College, Preston

No School

If I didn't have school today,
I would get up late
Then lie in bed all morning.

If I didn't have school today,
I would slowly get up,
Happy that I didn't have any work to do.

If I didn't have school today,
I would go to the park
And sit on the bench watching the birds.

If I didn't have school today,
I would slowly wander home, mid-afternoon,
In the warm sun.

If I didn't have school today,
I would watch a film all evening,
Not having to worry about homework.

If I didn't have school today,
I would go to bed when I wanted
And talk on the phone all night.

But that won't happen,
Because I have school today.

Olivia Jackson (12)
The Princess Helena College, Preston

Peer Pressure

'Come on Becky, take a snort!'
It's like I've forgotten what I've been taught:
Say no and push the drugs away
True friends will come to you someday.

'Come on Becky, it's just a beer!'
They seem to think that I can't hear,
But their words are ringing in my head,
Filling my whole mind with dread.

'Go on Bex, punch the little slag!'
They want me to take her handbag.
They've made me sniff and drink and steal,
Mum yells at me over the family meal.

I want to get good grades at school
But that's so 'totally not cool'.
They've got me hooked on cigarettes,
Something I'll always regret,
I thought there was a fire burning in my mouth,
'Shut up and put the damn thing out!'
So I carry on,
Smoking and stealing
And laughing and choking.
I want to stop
But they won't let me.

Rebecca Day (13)
The Princess Helena College, Preston

There Is A Hero In Us all

One day Meg awakes to a beautiful day
And wants to go to the dock of the bay.
She looks out of her window to see the sky
But instead she sees a strange thing go by.
It is green and blue with yellow too,
She watches and doesn't know what to do.
She thinks to herself, *what can it be?*
It's a monster, no doubt, she now can see.
She needs her hero
Who can help her so,
For the monster will not go.

Her great hero is a definite no show,
So she sits in her cupboard hiding away,
Praying for someone to say,
'Here I am, oh precious Meggy-moo,
I'm here to slay the monster for you.
I will beat him and kill him and keep him at bay,
Then we'll live happily and run away!
She summons her courage and holds her head high,
Then says, 'Today won't be the day I die!'

At the end of the day she wins the fight,
So now her future is very bright.
She is her own hero, all the way through,
We could learn something from her too.

Elika Siamak (13)
The Princess Helena College, Preston

Nineties To Noughties

Born in the nineties,
Living in the noughties.
Technical advances and changing fashions.
Sisters in their twenties, mother in her forties,
Teenage tantrums and perfect passions.

Back in the old days,
Sitting in a pushchair,
Looking up at everyone as they pass by.
Seeing all the colours of the clothes that they wear,
Terrible twos with that shrieking cry.

Finding a job
And leaving education,
Earning a wage and paying all the bills.
Who would have thought it is now my generation?
Time to put right all of the ills.

Hannah Nichols (13)
The Princess Helena College, Preston

What Has Happened?

I wake up,
I see no cars, no smoke, only an empty road.
What has happened?
The sky is blue,
The grass is green, not the usual clumps of mud.
Where is the world I'm used to?
No electricity,
No TV blaring, all I can hear is dead silence.
What has become of the world?
I step outside,
No horrible smell, not the usual smoky atmosphere,
What could it be?
No one is here,
No horns beeping, I quite like the silence.
Why has the world changed?
I will tell you what has happened,
We finally pulled our finger out
And saw what was happening to this wonderful planet.
That's what has happened!

Angharad Cook (12)
The Princess Helena College, Preston

Make The world A Fluffier Place

I was walking around the town one day
And I saw a fox fur coat,
I thought it was disgusting
And this I strongly note.

In the Chinese fur farms
Every year they make
300,000 seal cub coats,
Why can't they just use fake?

They set up traps in forests
All around the USA,
And leave them there to die sometimes,
Is there no nicer way?

They grab them from the back,
Then hang them by their legs,
It happens while they're still awake,
Just dangling from wooden pegs!

They strip them from the ankles,
Down to their little paws,
I love them when they're fluffy,
Not left dying on the floor!

They step on them and strangle them
Until they live no more,
So don't buy fur coats,
Don't fall for the lure . . .

Jodie Vallance (13)
The Princess Helena College, Preston

Who Is Perfect?

'I hate my hair,
It's frizzy and stupid.
But Kate is pretty.'

Rachel doesn't like the way she looks,
So Rachel isn't perfect.

'I hate failing tests,
I never understand what it's about.
But Phoebe is smart.'

Kate feels like she doesn't know anything,
So Kate isn't perfect.

'No one ever talks to me,
I'm never interesting.
But Rachel is funny.'

Phoebe thinks she is boring,
So Phoebe isn't perfect.

'Hey Rachel, new invention:
Hair straighteners!'
'Hey Kate, you must be so proud,
You got an E instead of an F!'
'Hey Phoebe, I like your top,
Grey suits your personality!'

Leah likes the way she looks.
Leah thinks she's smart.
Leah thinks she's fun.
So Leah must be perfect.
Right?

Ruth Couchman (12)
The Princess Helena College, Preston

It Can Happen

We see it on TV,
We read it in the paper,
But do we really know?

People say change the world,
People say save the whales,
People say make poverty history,
I say how?

I say get up,
I say take action,
I say we can,
I say together!

We can't do it in a day,
We can't do it in a month,
But we *can* do it!
One thing at a time,
One day at a time,
One act at a time . . .

So let's go . . .
It doesn't take magic,
It takes time,
It takes strength,
It takes passion,
It takes many.
Change.
Change the world.

Ellie Shewring (13)
The Princess Helena College, Preston

School Days

I wish I could make up a brilliant rule,
Choose all the lessons that are cool,
Make sure the teachers aren't too mean.
There's too much homework, that's obscene!

We get too stressed about a test
And all we do is try our best,
Then we don't get time to play,
Joke or even enjoy our day.

On top of that we have so much pressure
To do well while we are young,
So that when we try out for a job
They see how well we've done.

School is like a storybook,
There's no telling what you'll do,
So take a chance while you can,
It's really up to you.

Charlotte Whitelaw (13)
The Princess Helena College, Preston

Rugby

Rugby is fun
Rugby is great
The ball falls to the ground
We all fall in a state
The two teams hit each other
Everyone, it's Wilkinson!
See his shot
Is it a conversion?
Or maybe not.

Jack Earl (11)
West Hatch High School, Chigwell

Alone

The sweet smell of rose still floats in the air
But among the smell, a new one invades.
As the odour gets nearer I thrust myself away,
I do not like the smell.

Night came and so did the row,
Boom, bang, bash, was all I heard.
I am an only child with no sisters or brothers
And now nearly no parents . . .

The sun rose and a fresh new day arrived
But it didn't seem to change,
Except something hit me harder than ever,
'Let's divorce'!

Memories float into my head,
The sweet smell of rose lingered in my nostrils,
I long to hold her hand
But there will never be another chance.

The doorbell rings and I unfasten the lock,
His hair, his eyes, his nose, who is he?
My mother pushed past me and grabbed him by the arm,
He gave me one last look and they were gone.

My father looked me in my tear-filled eyes,
No one can replace the sweet scent of rose,
Especially the smell of lavender.

Denise Cheung (12)
West Hatch High School, Chigwell

What If . . . ?

Sometimes when I look around
All I can think is, *why are we here?*
What's our purpose?
What's our meaning of living?
What would the world be like if we weren't here?
What would it be like if there
Was no such thing as poverty?
Or even such a thing as money?
What would the world be like?
I wonder, I wonder . . .
What if, what if . . .
What if there wasn't such a thing as electricity?
Why do we have all of these things?
What if we all lived like the medieval people lived,
With no luxuries like we do today,
And with no money to pay?
What would we do all day?
Will this all turn out into some sort of story?
What becomes of you when you die?
Why is it that we can talk?
Why do we need to breathe to live?
No one will ever know the true meanings.
All we can do is question and wonder.
I wonder, I wonder,
What if, what if . . . ?

Zoe Bailey (13)
West Hatch High School, Chigwell

Going Around Town!

Me and my boys
Jamming in the hood,
Sitting around
Like most people should.
On my way to Toys 'R' Us,
All I was doing
Was catching the bus.
Some old woman
Started making a fuss,
She said, 'Excuse me,
I'll swipe you like dust.'
I said, 'Chill little lady,
You're driving me crazy.
Oh yeah, don't be afraid of me.
Take a chill pill like other people would,
Like I said, do what you should.'
Sorry about this brand new rap,
Don't think you could make a comeback.

Todd Sheridan (11)
West Hatch High School, Chigwell

The Butterfly

Fluttering swiftly through the sky,
It is a beautiful butterfly,
With its delicate wings
Shimmering in the sunlight,
Discreetly flying up in the trees,
Visiting flowers with bumblebees.
Magnificent patterned wings,
Vivid colours of pink and blue,
Along it goes, high and low,
With dazzling gems of indigo.
Graceful and elegant it flies away,
Hoping to live another day.

Hannah Broadbent (12)
West Hatch High School, Chigwell

Lonely Little Girl

My life isn't that exciting,
I'm a good girl, I don't like fighting.
I go to school every day and come back,
On the way home I go to see the swans, who quack.
I get straight As,
I get them nearly every day.
I don't have many friends
Because when I meet them,
The relationship always bends.
Me and people . . . we just don't go,
So I'm always on my own.
I get teased quite a lot,
And sometimes I wish I was shot.
See . . .
I told you my life wasn't interesting.
Well . . . bye.

Selina Suri (12)
West Hatch High School, Chigwell

Seasons

It was a hot summer's day,
The sun was shining,
The birds were singing.
Now autumn's on its way
And has pushed summer away.
The leaves are golden brown,
The conkers are growing,
It starts to get colder,
The blackberries start growing.
The air is cold and gets colder,
As cold as ice.
The autumn goes
And winter returns.

Grace Anderson (13)
West Hatch High School, Chigwell

Kids Today!

Don't you remember when we were in Year 2,
When we used to play happily, only me and you?
But now that we are growing up
And we are in Year 8,
We both have got boyfriends
And we go on double dates.
We used to have a lot of fun.
All of the boys had 'cooties'
And weren't considered hot.
You still can't remember?
I can't believe you forgot!
You have to remember
When we were in Year 4!
When it came to chocolate
We'd just want more and more.
But now that we're older
And we are in Year 8,
We do not touch the food
Because we want to watch our weight.
I wish we were back in primary school,
Because I want to run around
And act just like a fool.

Poppy Barker (12)
West Hatch High School, Chigwell

Just Another Day

A tiny yawn for some,
But a big one for me,
Still big enough to be heard
And Mummy's face I see.

Her big arms wrap around me,
She gives me a big smile,
And after all of that sleep
It all seems worthwhile.

Daddy's turn to feed me,
Just one more bite,
Watch my favourite film
And we call it a night.

It's not an easy job
Being a 2-year-old,
And what about tomorrow?
To the park maybe?

A tiny yawn for some,
But a big one for me,
Nothing else to be heard,
And darkness I see.

Kathryn Hopper (13)
West Hatch High School, Chigwell

What Are We Doing Here?

Have you ever thought
About how we came to be?
Floating around, so small and alone,
In a universe huge and free.

Some say it doesn't matter,
Living their life as it is.
Others care too much,
Wondering why we exist.

Is it survival of the fittest?
Looking only for one's own gain,
Making too much money,
Then spending it on games.

Or should we help each other?
Keeping a community,
Living all together,
In a crowd, not just me, me, me!

When we think all about it,
So many answers give us the blues,
But all I have to say is
At least we are free to choose.

Eloise Shepherd (13)
West Hatch High School, Chigwell

Our Generation!

What is the meaning of life?
Why are we here?
More people die by the knife,
Others live in fear.
This is our generation.

There are more gangs on the street,
Younger people drinking, smoking and taking drugs,
More people in poverty, nothing to eat,
These teenagers, we call them thugs.
This is our generation.

We are afraid to go out at night,
Our parents are more protective,
In case we get a fright,
If we make new friends they are very selective.
This is our generation.

Darkness is upon us,
Everyone is scared,
Families make a fuss,
As they care.
This is our generation.

Caroline Huxley (12)
West Hatch High School, Chigwell

The Great Game

We were all waiting,
We were all excited
As England and Brazil walked out.
The crowd started to cheer,
The game was about to begin.

The weather was snowy,
It was cold everywhere.
England V Brazil was almost going to start.
Then the whistle went,
The game had begun.

Beckham got the ball,
He did not let England down.
As he scored the goal
The crowd started to cheer.
The first half had ended.

The second half began,
Ronaldinho got the ball,
He shot, he scored a great goal.
The crowd was waiting,
Minutes to go,
Rooney got the ball,
He shot and he scored.

The crowd went loud.
The final score:
England 2, Brazil 1.
What a game.

Bobby Eavy (112)
West Hatch High School, Chigwell

Confusion

Millions of thoughts are rushing through my head
I try to sleep it off as I lay in my bed.
Buzzing around like thousands of bees
These crazy thoughts just will not ease.

I try to be happy, I've tried really hard
But the unease that I'm feeling is stronger by far.
The school bell has rung, here we go again,
I hope today it will get better or otherwise when?

I care about education and want to be smart
But if this bullying gets worse will these feelings depart?
I hope this time will make me stronger
As I know I have to stay here for much longer.

Walking through the long hallways
These anxiety pains happen always.
I long to go home and curl up in bed
These tears building up I long to shed.

I have this weight on my shoulders
Weighing me down like rocks or boulders.
This can get better, I know it can
But I'm the one who makes it happen.

I am strong and will get through this
Maybe things will get better if I could just tell Miss.
Although would that help? I just don't know.
I feel like I'm trapped under a pile of snow.

Millions of thoughts are rushing through my head
I try to sleep it off as I lay in my bed.
Buzzing around like thousands of bees
These crazy thoughts just will not ease.

Nadine Archer (12)
West Hatch High School, Chigwell

My Generation

My generation has a lot of expectation,
It's up to us to look after our civilisation,

Guns and knives and more weapons too,
Any of these could be used on you,

Mobile phones and computers as well,
Just buying one or two could make us excel,

Tobacco is a drug which you can smoke,
But when you get addicted, it ain't no joke,

It's 2008,
And the Third World's in a state,

We have lots to do,
But we all need you!

Olivia Smith (13)
West Hatch High School, Chigwell

White Blanket

It is Sunday,
Easter Sunday,
Snow is falling to the ground
Forming a beautiful white blanket.
A blanket of hope?
Each snowflake is unique,
Creating a mesmerising pattern across the sky,
Falling silently.
They look so graceful,
So pretty.
I am warm in my dressing gown,
Drinking my hot chocolate.
Birds up high in the trees,
Watching the snow fall.
Snow keeps falling,
Beginning to melt as the sun comes out.

Hannah Shanley (13)
West Hatch High School, Chigwell

Four Little Lions

Four little lions
Sitting in a tree,
One became a lady's coat,
Now there's only three.

Three little lions,
'Neath a sky of blue,
One became a rich man's rug,
Now there's only two.

Two little lions
Sleeping under the sun,
One a hunter's trophy made,
Now there's only one.

One little lion,
Waiting to be had.
Oops! He got the hunter first,
Aren't you kind of glad?

Georgina Cross (13)
West Hatch High School, Chigwell

Football

The silence before the whistle blows,
The thoughts come rushing but no one knows,
A six-pointer, the papers say,
A must win game we have to play.

A hard fought game from the start,
The tackles flying from every part,
From one end to another,
Victory was just a goal away,
The joy or sadness was soon to sow,
How the game began to ebb and flow.
The whistle blown, oh how the game has flown.

Victory, the cup is ours,
Today we are the glowing stars.

James Philips (12)
West Hatch High School, Chigwell

Seasons

The clouds in the sky were thin,
The ghostly breeze tickled my skin,
The flowers began to bloom,
Chasing away winter's gloom.
It was the perfect night in spring.

The night sky was clear,
The sound of birds was all you could hear,
The warm breeze,
People with hayfever sneeze.
It was the perfect night in summer.

Stars dotted the night sky,
Planes flew silently by,
The wind blew,
The leaves flew.
It was the perfect night in autumn.

Snow blanketed the cold ground,
The wind whistling was the only sound,
The cold air,
The trees bare.
It was the perfect night in winter.

Reshma Khalique (12)
West Hatch High School, Chigwell

Young Writers Information

We hope you have enjoyed reading this book - and that you will continue to enjoy it in the coming years.

If you like reading and writing poetry drop us a line, or give us a call, and we'll send you a free information pack.

Alternatively if you would like to order further copies of this book or any of our other titles, then please give us a call or log onto our website at www.youngwriters.co.uk

Young Writers Information
Remus House
Coltsfoot Drive
Peterborough
PE2 9JX

(01733) 890066